COMBAT AND SURVIVAL
WHAT IT TAKES TO FIGHT AND WIN

VOLUME
19

Originally published in the United Kingdom in weekly parts **COMBAT & SURVIVAL**
is a study of the armed forces at work. It shows the skills taught to soldiers
and the way in which military units operate. It examines the weapons
and equipment used by different armies; and, by looking at recruit
training and exercises, **COMBAT & SURVIVAL** demonstrates
how the armed forces develop individual responsibility,
leadership and initiative.

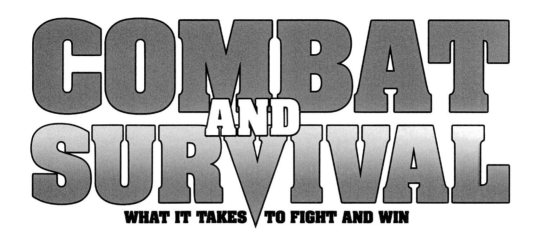

COMBAT AND SURVIVAL

WHAT IT TAKES TO FIGHT AND WIN

VOLUME
19

H. S. STUTTMAN, INC. *publishers*   Westport, Connecticut 06889

Contents

Volume 19

Published by H. S. STUTTMAN INC.
Westport, Connecticut 06889
© Aerospace Publishing 1991
ISBN 0-87475-560-3

HELICOPTER ASSAULT TACTICS

The cabin of a troop-carrying helicopter going into battle is a confusing place. The noise is truly ear-shattering, and every available space is cluttered with essential equipment and a jostling crowd of excited men keyed up to fever pitch. Time after time heliborne operations ('heliops') have proved their worth in anti-terrorist and counter-insurgency campaigns. This is the first section on Bush Warfare, and shows how the South African Defence Force uses helicopters as combat and support craft in anti-terrorist operations.

The helicopter's main strength in combat is its ability to get troops into areas that they could otherwise reach only on foot, perhaps after days of cross-country marching. It gets them there so quickly that a successful operation can be mounted before the enemy has any idea that they're aware of his presence.

Because airborne operations take place at such high speed, it's extra-important that each member of the aircrew and the airborne troop knows exactly what he has to do at all times. Helicopters are expensive to operate – every hour of flight costs many hundreds of pounds – and have only a short radius of action.

Know your job

Helicopter drill has two purposes: to cut down time wasted through mistakes; and to make sure that both aircraft and personnel stay as safe as possible. There are no short cuts. Everyone concerned has to do things

---

STICK LEADER'S PRE-FLIGHT DUTIES

As the leader of the stick, you must make a series of checks before the helicopter is airborne. Once in the air you use the spare headset to communicate with the pilots and keep an eye on the ground over which you will be operating.

1. Brief the men on the signals that will be used during emplaning and deplaning.
2. Ensure that everyone has taken off their caps or jungle hats.
3. Check that no-one is loosely carrying equipment such as water bottles, machetes, ammunition pouches etc.
4. Make sure that all straps on packs and equipment are tucked away.
5. Remove the aerials from the radios and stow them away.
6. Check that weapon slings are tight, carrying handles folded down and that bayonets are not fixed.
7. Check that all weapons safety precautions have been observed.

Fire Force in action: South African soldiers fly into action aboard an Aérospatiale Puma helicopter. They are kept on standby to launch instant attacks on terrorist gangs the moment they are discovered by patrols, hidden observers or aerial reconnaissance.

20 metres at 2 o'clock

The troops enter the helicopter in reverse of the order they will leave the aircraft. When boarding and during the flight, the following precautions must be observed:

1 Your rifle must have an empty breech and the safety must be applied.
2 Leave your bayonet in your scabbard; do not attach it to your rifle.
3 Take your hat off and tuck it in your webbing

exactly by the book. When the order comes to start a heliborne operation, the stick leader must make sure that each member of the team knows his place and what to do immediately after leaving the aircraft. He should form his squad up in the reverse of the order they will leave the aircraft. Then he waits for the pilot's signal to emplane – a clear nod of the head and a thumbs-up sign, for example. When in the helicopter it is vital that no infantryman interferes with the crew, and that no one touches any of the controls.

Overwhelming noise

The noise in a helicopter is quite deafening. The stick leader should always put on the spare headset so that he can communicate with the pilot and any other crew members.

Weapons safety, at all times, is vitally important. A round fired off by accident could hit a vital piece of machinery and cost the life of everyone aboard. For this reason weapons must be carried with the breech cleared. On those rare occasions when the stick has to come out of the aircraft fighting, then the weapon can be charged and cocked, but the safety must be on, to make it impossible to loose off a round by accident. Because of the cramped conditions, bayonets should never in any circumstances be fixed on board.

The man in charge

The pilot is in command of the aircraft at all times. He is responsible for it, and for every person on board. His commands must be obeyed immediately. He alone decides how many men can be carried, and when and how they will enter and leave the aircraft. For operational reasons, he transmits his orders through the stick commander.

The stick commander also has his

Troops relax en route to the landing zone in the operational area up-country in southern Africa. The mood will soon change once they've landed in a hostile area.

own responsibilities. These are mainly to do with the safety of his men and how they behave in the aircraft, but he must also pay attention to the ground they are above, looking for possible future landing sites, useful terrain features such as sources of fresh water and potential defensive positions, and, of course, signs of the enemy.

Contact!

The real strength of heliborne counter-insurgency operations is the speed with which they can be mounted. Experience of actual operations has

shown SADF that concealed static observation posts are much more effective in gathering intelligence about enemy movements than mobile patrols. A patrol moving cross-country gives itself away very easily, especially by being seen and reported to guerrillas by civilian sympathisers. These static OPs must be in constant

LANDING ZONE PROCEDURES

Just as counter-insurgency troops rely on the helicopter crew to get them safely in and out of the battle, the pilot and crew depend on the men on the ground to carry out certain tasks.

Clearing and marking the LZ is the most important job. A heavily-laden helicopter can't land or take off straight up and down. When it's full of cargo or passengers, it behaves more like

an ordinary aircraft, and must land and take off at a shallow angle. A track must be cleared so that the pilot can bring the aircraft safely into and out of the LZ.

Another advantage the helicopter does have over fixed-wing aircraft, however, is that it is much less influenced by the wind direction when landing and at take-off. Instead of having to head into the wind at take-off, the

helicopter pilot has a wider choice: he only has to pay attention to wind direction when it's really strong. This in turn makes the ground crew's job a lot easier – the same LZ can be used in all sorts of conditions.

At night the LZ must be marked with lights. Five is the best number, arranged in the shape of a T, with the top bar into the wind if this is important. Otherwise the bar will be opposite the shallowest possible approach path.

Battery torches are a good source of light. They should be placed 10 metres apart, with the beams shining up at an angle of

Puma landing zone

To land safely, a Puma helicopter needs a landing zone at least 50 metres in diameter, with a central area 35 metres in diameter cleared to ground level. At the centre of the LZ there must be a hard surface 15 metres in diameter.

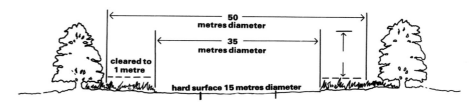

50 metres diameter
35 metres diameter
cleared to 1 metre
hard surface 15 metres diameter

HAND SIGNALS

The noise inside a helicopter makes voice communications practically impossible so hand signals are used:

Prepare to deplane: Pilot or crew member motions with his left hand.

Emplaning signal (day): Pilot or crew member gives the thumbs up or vigorously nods his head. It is now safe to approach the helicopter (in a stooped attitude, to avoid the rotors).

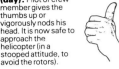

Emplaning signal (night): Intermittent flashing of the helicopter navigation lights.

Do not emplane yet: Pilot or crew member raises open right hand with the palm outwards.

Some members of the stick to emplane: Pilot or crew member extends a number of fingers indicating how many men are to board the helicopter.

Target direction: This is indicated by the pilot or crew member pointing.

Deplane: Pilot or crew member nods his head vigorously. You must now exit the plane in the pre-arranged order as fast as you can.

SEATING PLAN

1 The stick leader is last into and first out of the helicopter.
2 The LMG crews sit nearest the doors and operate the machine-guns as protection.
3 In a crisis, 24 men may be loaded, at sea level only.

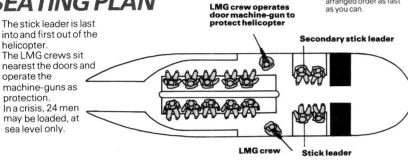

LMG crew operates door machine-gun to protect helicopter

Secondary stick leader

LMG crew   Stick leader

radio contact with the operational base.

When a report of terrorist activity comes in, it should be only a matter of moments before assault troops are called together for a briefing. This will include all the essential information about the contact: map reference, a short report of the circumstances, the number of assault troops required, whether they are to be supported by helicopter gunships or other air strikes, how they are to approach the target, rendezvous (RV) position with troops already on the ground, and the radio frequencies, call signs and passwords that are to be used for the operation.

All this can be accomplished in the time it takes the aircrews to warm up the helicopters and carry out their pre-launch checks. Within minutes, the assault sticks can be out on the dispersal point, waiting for the signal to emplane.

Troop commander

The troop commander always travels in the helicopter gunship. If there is no gunship support, he has to travel in the lead troop carrier. Where a gunship is involved in the operation, it must be possible for friendly ground forces to identify it easily. The best way to achieve this is by means of a series of smoke grenades, tied to the step or undercarriage of the gunship, and triggered by the troop commander.

Going in to land

When the assault force arrives at the RV, contact with the forces who have spotted the enemy will make sure that the commander has up-to-date information about the guerrillas' behaviour. While the troop carriers orbit the RV on a high and wide course, the ship carrying the troop commander goes in low, so that he can see the enemy disposition for himself. The observers in the static OP should have reported the presence of any anti-aircraft weaponry with the guerrilla band, and the troop commander must bear this in mind when deciding how close to the enemy he can get. Where

---

between 30 and 40 degrees. Because the helicopter's main rotor generates a very powerful down-draught, the torches must be partly buried in the ground, to prevent them being blown over.

If there are more than five torches to hand, the number of individual lights is not increased. Instead, two torches are used at each location, one angled as before, the other pointing straight up into the sky.

Other light sources can be used instead of torches. Hurricane lamps or pressure lamps are both good enough and, as a last resort, sand in an open-ended tin can be soaked with a gallon of petrol and set alight. The helicopter pilot will bring his craft to land slightly to the left of the three lights that form the vertical line of the T, so the lights are best placed slightly to the right of centre of the LZ.

In an emergency, vehicle headlamps can be used to mark the LZ. Parked at the edge of the cleared area, the vehicles should be between 20 and 25 metres apart, and angled at 45 degrees so that their headlights meet in the centre of the landing zone. The aircraft will approach them from behind, and come in between the vehicles, so they must not have radio aerials sticking up.

Vehicle-lit emergency night landing zone

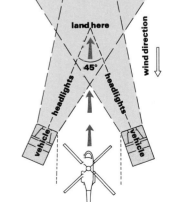

land here

wind direction

45°

vehicle headlights   vehicle headlights

vehicle   vehicle

Position two vehicles 25 metres apart and facing into the wind. Turn them slightly towards each other so that the intersection of their headlights forms an angle of 45°. This will be the helicopter's landing point.

Night landing
To guide a helicopter onto the landing zone at night, lay out five lights in a 'T' shape pointing into the wind. Lights can be either lamps dug into the ground or torches pointing towards the direction the helicopter will be coming from. Put each light 10 paces apart.

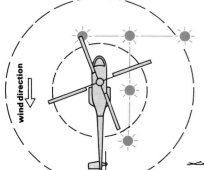

wind direction

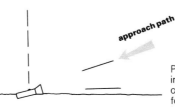

approach path

Troops must exit or enter the helicopter at incredible speed: in one operation in Angola, paratroopers had to clamber on board while under fire from a Cuban tank!

possible, the gunship should go in close to soften up the enemy with strafing fire before troops go in on the ground.

On the troop commander's signal, the transports will come down to prearranged positions in the LZ (landing zone). Where possible, they will touch down, but over rougher terrain such as long grass or badly broken

DEPLANING PROCEDURE

The troops must exit the helicopter as fast as possible, throwing packs out of the door and assuming an all-round defensive position. The two machine-gun (LMG) crews must exit first to provide covering fire for the rest of the stick. Normally the helicopter will land to emplane or deplane personnel but over long grass, bushes or uneven terrain, men and equipment are dropped while the helicopter hovers at between 1.2 and 1.8 m. In order to prevent the aircraft from rocking too much when the troops depart from a hovering helicopter they must not leap out sideways, but drop straight to the ground from the steps provided.

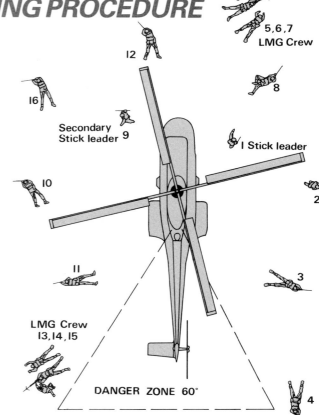

5,6,7 LMG Crew

8

12

16

Secondary Stick leader 9

1 Stick leader

10

2

3

11

LMG Crew 13,14,15

DANGER ZONE 60°

4

Aérospatiale Puma
The Puma is one of the main helicopters used by the South African Defence Force. It flies at treetop height to avoid anti-aircraft fire, which now includes heat seeking SA-7 missiles supplied by the Soviet Union.

Troopers and their kit
Each stick (helicopter-load of troops) must be prepared for an extended period of operations on the ground, pursuing and fighting the terrorists. In the dense bush it is easy for a stick to become isolated, so it must be able to communicate, navigate and defend itself against superior enemy forces. The stick leader should have a ground/air radio, a map, compass and protractor plus mini-flare and heliograph. The men must have rations and bedding for prolonged operations but should otherwise be lightly equipped. Everyone should carry a torch, as patrolling often involves searching native huts. In case the stick bumps into a large concentration of terrorists it must include at least one gun group with a light machine-gun.

ground they will stay in a low hover, one or two metres above the ground. Troops must be prepared to jump out, making sure they have all their equipment with them, and being careful not to upset the aircraft in the process — something that happens all too easily to a hovering helicopter. Unless they are in hot pursuit, with the enemy in sight, troops will make a defensive ring around the aircraft. Each trooper knows his position in the defensive structure, and goes to it without being told.

Trying to hide

Rather than try to run for it, insurgents may choose instead to go to ground, hoping to escape by hiding. This is especially true in open country. This means that pursuing forces have to be prepared to mount lengthy search operations whenever they are sent in to eliminate a guerrilla group. This causes a number of problems: it becomes necessary to re-supply with rations, to carry bedding and survival equipment and to have enough weaponry and ammunition for every conceivable circumstance.

In search and tracking operations, the fighting forces also need the help and support of specialists — especially intelligence officers and dogs and men trained in search and tracking techniques. The helicopter is the usual means of transport for these, to get the right people into the right place in the shortest possible time.

As soon as the ground forces have been deployed from the aircraft, most of the helicopters will return to the nearest defended supply base, where

The Rhodesians pioneered the Fire Force System, although their resources were very limited. This is an Alouette III spotting for a mortar shoot against an enemy position.

they can be immediately refuelled and made ready to return to the combat zone. One or two craft will remain within a very short flight-time of the ground forces, to be available to move troops from place to place within the combat zone if this becomes necessary.

Fire Force

The Fire Force technique uses helicopter-borne troops to launch surprise attacks on terrorist groups. The troops are kept at instant readiness so that the moment a terrorist group is detected in the operational zone, troops can be airborne and on their way. Aircraft and helicopter gunships are used to soften up landing zones before the vulnerable troop-carrying helicopters come in to land.

Stick leader
During flight, the stick leader's job is to communicate with the aircrew, look out for enemy movement on the ground and to build up a mental picture of possible landing zones, dropping zones and watering holes that might be of use on this or future missions.

Combat Report
Vietnam:
Airfield Perimeter Duty

The sprawling American air bases in Vietnam were a favourite Viet Cong target. Here a US Air Force security policeman describes some of his experiences on perimeter duty at Tan Son Nhut.

At this time our ARVN allies had control of the outer perimeter where we had set up LPs. This perimeter was guarded by concertina wire, Claymore mines, trip flares, punji stakes and a Free Fire Zone. A little way off was our army, who took care of their perimeter and the ARVN's. The ARVN weren't very well trained: they tended to fire a few rounds and then retreat. Conversely, our army was good. We were also better equipped, and had the advantage of helicopter gunships, including the Huey Cobra.

The daylight hours were normally quiet, except during the rainy season. Just my luck to be put on perimeter duty at this time. With the rain you're cold and soggy all the time, and you run the risk of getting trench foot.

I just opened fire

It was on such a rainy night that I killed my first person. I was positioned near our planes. On these nights there was always sniper fire, and sometimes a few VC would get through and make for the planes. I was wet and tired and had just had a three-day drinking session, and wasn't really up to par. So I got a shock when the shooting started around midnight.

Daniels, who was a few feet to my left, and Mouth, who was on my right, said they had seen something move. They were preparing to open fire when suddenly, right in front of me, someone jumped up and started running towards me. I really didn't have time to think: I just opened fire and hoped it was one of them. I usually kept my weapon on safe, then switched to single fire if anything happened. This time it happened so fast I switched to auto. I got him full in the chest, and was going for another when there was an explosion that knocked me back and threw mud and stuff all over me. Daniels and Mouth had opened fire and got the other two. Mouth was wounded by the charge that went off; he lost an ear and some skin.

We held our positions until the STT teams and a medic arrived. The VC we'd killed were only

dressed in shorts, but they had enough explosives strapped to them to take out a whole squadron. All, that is, except the one I'd killed: there wasn't enough left of him to put in a thimble.

I had never killed anyone before. In the towers we had shot people, but who's to say whose bullet killed who. And up there you couldn't see them properly. This time it was different.

In the forward positons there were two dead GIs. Both had been smoking dope and had figured that the ARVN up ahead would take care of any sappers, but the ARVN had moved as soon as the sniper fire started up. We often moved too, to avoid becoming sitting ducks, but we informed each other when we did so. The ARVN hadn't bothered, and it cost two men's lives and left one wounded.

It always seemed as if the VC got more daring just before our holiday seasons. I guess they thought we were more relaxed, and thinking of home and families. First they would create a diversion, either by rockets or sniper fire. Then they would try to infiltrate our lines. We lost more airplanes to the rockets than to sappers.

A Christmas truce?

There was one night when a couple of sappers got through. It was a quiet night, no rain for once, but a lot of ground fog because of the rice paddies. They got through without a shot being fired, and made it to a squadron of F-4 Phantoms before a security cop opened up on them. He managed to hold them off until help came, and when it did arrive all hell broke out. One cop was killed and three were wounded. A plane was lost, and two others were damaged.

I was on the perimeter for two weeks, then on the ammo area. This place was more secure: it was practically under ground and covered by sandbags. It was also surrounded by five-metre fences, with gun towers at each corner and one in the middle with two M-60 machine-guns inside. Again I was in a tower, at least for part of the time. The rest of the time was spent at the control entry point or riding around inside the fence perimeter.

We had heard rumours of a Christmas truce, but the guys who had been there the previous Christmas knew better. Somehow the VC were becoming quite accurate at zeroing in, not only on aircraft but also on the ammo storage areas. Apparently an investigation was under way to see who or what was helping the VC. In the

meantime we were extra cautious along our perimeter, around the planes and in the ammo areas.

It was right after the truce began for Christmas that the VC launched an attack. They were going for the planes. Most of us were off duty at the time, preparing for Christmas dinner, when we were put on alert and dispatched to the airfield and ammo points. I was thankful for our APCs, as rockets were falling everywhere. Luckily I think their aim was off that day, because a couple of barracks were hit.

It made our teeth rattle

Four APCs surrounded the ammo area, and we waited. That was scary: there you were in a tin can, with shells falling all around you. I kept asking Sgt Peterson if we could get out and dig in around the area. He thought about this but decided against it: he said we were too close to the treeline for them to hit us. Then a shell landed so close it made our teeth rattle.

The sergeant was manning the 50-cal with the hatch open when the shell hit. When he came down he was as white as a sheet. Only then did he tell everyone to get out and take cover. I mumbled something about it being a bit late, but we all got out and headed for the treeline.

It had been going on for over an hour and still no let-up. I was wondering where the hell our choppers, army and artillery were. You could hear choppers everywhere, and every now and then one would fly over, but so far they hadn't had any effect on the VC mortars.

Another shell hit just by the APC. Later, when it was all over, we discovered that it was full of shrapnel holes. Our ammo point had been hit in the back side and one of the towers was at a crazy angle, and the guard was nowhere to be seen. Another hit on the fence caused a large hole, but so far there hadn't been a direct hit. If only we could see what to shoot at. Smoke was coming from the flight line; they had obviously hit a plane or two.

Finally, our radio came to life and we were given the all clear. But I don't think anyone had asked the VC, since they didn't stop for another 20 minutes. Altogether we lost three planes and one chopper, and had 16 dead and 22 wounded. What a merry Christmas.

US Air Force security police move out to the perimeter of Tan Son Nhut during an attack by the Viet Cong in February 1968.

An exhausted airman lies on a box of supplies in the wake of a Viet Cong attack. Smoke rises from burning fuel tanks ignited by guerrilla mortars.

AMBUSHING THE TERRORISTS

In the brush and long grass near a bend in the rough track leading to a guerrilla staging area, you can hear a leaf drop, but it's an artificial silence. The whole area is stiff with men of Y Company, 5th South African Infantry Battalion, waiting for a group of insurgents that, they know, includes a local terrorist chief. Their task: to take the top man alive and dispose of as many of the others as possible. Standing-by in the rear are trackers and their dogs, ready to go off in hot pursuit of any terrorist who might escape the ambush. At the nearest hardened defensive position, helicopters wait to carry the attack force on follow-up operations.

A fine art

In this section on counter-insurgency tactics, taken from the South African Defence Force (SADF) manual on anti-terrorist operations, you'll discover how they set up and follow up ambush operations. Since 1965, when SADF began anti-terrorist operations (ATOPS), they have developed the ambush into a fine art.

Above: South African troops at the scene of a terrorist murder in South West Africa in which a farmer was killed by a landmine buried in the road. SWAPO (South West Africa Peoples Organisation) has waged a terrorist campaign for the last 20 years and since 1975 has received considerable assistance from Angola and its Soviet allies.

Members of 21 Battalion, South African Defence Force, practise night-firing techniques essential for anti-terrorist warfare. Better weapons training and fire control enable units of the security forces to defeat equal-sized units of terrorists.

The key to a successful ambush

1 **A high standard of training in ambushing techniques.**
2 **Careful planning.**
3 **Total security at all stages.**
4 **Good concealment techniques.**
5 **Intelligent siting of the ambush.**
6 **Good battle discipline, especially at night.**
7 **Accurate shooting from all positions.**

Most ambushes are laid as a result of information received from informers, from captured terrorists who break down under interrogation, or from agents operating clandestinely within the enemy organisation. Or the ambush may be the result of months spent in long and painstaking analysis of enemy movements using information from many sources.

Sometimes an ambush is designed to take out as many of the enemy as possible, or it may have just one very important person as its target.

The men for the job

The size of the squad to be used in the operation is decided very early on. It may range from four men to an entire company – but will be no bigger than is absolutely necessary. The smaller the force, the easier it is to infiltrate the position undetected, and the less their chance of giving themselves away while they're lying-up, waiting for the target to arrive at the killing ground.

The men sent on the operation will be the best available, even if that means splitting up established fighting teams temporarily. It's not unusual to find a company commander leading a six-man ambush group, if this is what offers the best chance of success. Because a successful ambush depends more than anything else on timing, the troops must be very strong on discipline. Their fieldcraft, too, must be superb. They must be able to move into their positions without leaving any trace.

Planning the operation

Because ambushes are often planned a long time ahead, the attack force commander can decide exactly the way things will go – and can even rehearse it, if he can find a similar-looking site far enough away from the actual attack area. However, this delay between the operation being planned and getting it under way makes for security problems. A few words overheard in a bar, or even in barracks where there might be civilian workers who are sympathetic to the enemy, can be enough to ruin the operation. Or, worse still, the enemy may set up a counter-operation. Standing orders are not to talk about the op. Not among yourselves, not on the telephone, not even in letters home.

Signals and commands

Only a good signalling system allows the commander to be in complete control of the operation, and that's essential. Every member of the attack force must know instantly when to start firing, cease fire, switch to secondary targets, regroup, commence follow-up operations, and call the operation off.

Often, commands will be given by signal, which means that the commander must be placed where the men can see him. The command position can be at the head or the tail of the ambush. If it's at the head, the commander can decide when to give the all-important order to open fire. As that may not be the best place for him to control the rest of the action, he usually places himself at the tail and leaves that job to his second in command.

Hold your fire
You should not open fire as long as the terrorists are moving closer towards someone who is in a better firing position. But if a terrorist acts as if he has spotted the ambush, you must open fire immediately.

The Ambush

Ambushes are the most effective method of dealing with terrorists. It is important to take full advantage of every chance offered: good intelligence information should be the basis for a carefully planned operation by specially selected troops.

Signal to fire
The commander can start the ambush by signalling to a machine-gun group in a different position. When the terrorists move away from the machine-gun fire, they unwittingly move deeper into the main killing ground.

Any member of the attack force is permitted to get the action going by opening fire, however, and the standing orders are to do that if anyone suspects he's been spotted by the enemy. The call-off signal is most important. There have been cases of one or two groups not receiving that signal and staying in place, then opening up on members of their own team, later.

Getting into position

When you're setting up an ambush, you must treat the local population as hostile. Move into action in absolute

Planning the ambush

Remember the following three points when planning the layout of an ambush:

1 Approaches
Intelligence information may well lead you to expect the enemy to approach from one particular direction but, however good your information, they may actually come from somewhere else. Your ambush should cover all approaches.

2 Killing ground
A cunningly-selected killing ground is the key to a good ambush. The enemy must be surprised and caught in a cross-fire from which there is no escape.

3 Depth
Experience has shown that the terrorists scatter with amazing speed at the first burst of fire. You must have other ambush groups positioned to shoot down those enemy who escape the opening burst.

Watching rota
Before the ambush is set, the commander must lay down a rota whereby some men remain on full alert while others relax in position, since it is impossible for everyone to remain totally alert for six to eight hours.

Waiting for the terrorists
The ambush party is keyed up, awaiting the approach of the enemy. It is often impossible to recognise the identity of the people entering an ambush area, particularly after dusk. This makes it essential for other security forces to stay out of the area to avoid accidents.

Shoot to kill
All shots must be aimed to kill. Only at the beginning of the ambush are you likely to have a clear target: make the most of it. Once the ambush is sprung they will become difficult, and you must be prepared to stand up to engage fast-moving targets.

Keeping still
Once the ambush group is in position, there must be no movement and no noise. This is a great test of discipline: you have to be able to get into a comfortable position and wait with weapons cocked and ready.

Springing the trap

The attack party is divided up into 'fire groups', although a 'group' may consist of just one machine-gunner. The first and last fire groups are called the stop groups and are usually machine-gunners. Their job is just what their name indicates – they're there to stop the enemy force moving, either forward down the track, or back the way it came. The ambush site is always chosen to force the enemy to decide between facing withering machine gun fire, or heading off the track into difficult terrain, where his progress will be reduced to a few metres a minute at best.

Ambushes are often placed on bends in the road so that the fleeing enemy forces will become concentrated in one place. They all run straight off the road, as they see it, away from the fire from the outside of the bend, but in fact this packs them close together in the real killing ground, which is the inside of the bend.

Spread out between the stop groups are the

secrecy. This might mean going in under cover of darkness the night before the ambush is going to take place, getting into concealment and staying there.

If the waiting period is going to be less than about nine hours, the force is divided into two "shifts", one on the alert, the other resting in their hiding places. They will live off the basic rations that each man carries. There must be no smoking, no lighting of fires or stoves, and absolutely no talking.

Living arrangements

If the waiting period goes into days, then much more complex living arrangements will have to be made. If possible, a rest area should be set up, far enough away from the ambush site not to give it away. Paths will have to be cleared between the rest area and the ambush zone so that movements can be made in silence.

If the ambush party is big, it should be split into three. One group will be on the alert, one resting at their posts, the third back in the rest area. At

Accurate shooting at night is very difficult, but it can be devastatingly effective if the troops are trained well. Plant sticks in the ground to fix the arcs of fire of each weapon to avoid accidentally shooting into your own men.

change-over time the alert party drops back to the rest area, the second party goes on to the alert and the party from the rest area moves up to become the reserve.

Even in a long-term ambush, all food should be pre-cooked, and you must have an adequate supply of water.

Night ambushes

Terrorists prefer to move at night, so that is when you most often have to attack them. It's relatively easy to stay hidden at night, but much more difficult to shoot accurately without some form of illumination, and the ambush commander has to consider this when he's planning the operation.

Automatic weapons will be fired on fixed lines at night, and the arc of fire of personal weapons must be controlled – probably by planting sticks in the ground to limit the movement to left and right – to reduce the danger of firing on a team-mate.

Night communications

The communications system has to be changed, too, for the visual silent system that you'd use in the daytime won't work at night, and you certainly can't use signal lamps. Hand contact signals or signal cords can both be effective, if clumsy. To make communications easier the groups should be closer together by night than by day.

It's important, too, that the ambush party stays absolutely still. Then you can be sure that any movement is enemy movement, and you can safely fire on it.

The attack force should be in position before nightfall – even if that

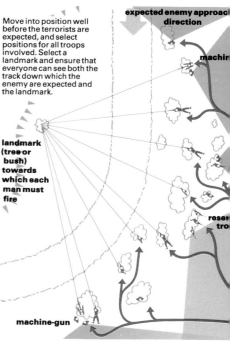

Move into position well before the terrorists are expected, and select positions for all troops involved. Select a landmark and ensure that everyone can see both the track down which the enemy are expected and the landmark.

expected enemy approach direction

landmark (tree or bush) towards which each man must fire

machine

reserve troop

machine-gun

means actually moving up the night before the attack and lying-up all day.

Any terrorists who have managed to get away from the killing ground will probably go to earth and try to hide until the attack force has gone. The best way to flush them out is with dogs – the smell of sweat from fear and exertion will lead the dogs straight to them. This means that the dog force must be close at hand, ready to go into action as soon as the first phase of the attack is over.

Close sweep

If dogs aren't available, the best alternative is a tight close-order sweep, with the force's automatic weapons placed to take out any terrorist flushed by the line of beaters. Search the area thoroughly and carefully, and try to match the body count with estimates of the terrorist group's original strength.

Prisoners must be kept apart from

Some common mistakes

1 Weapons uncocked, or with the safety on. The mechanical noise of doing either is a dead giveaway in the jungle or bush. Be ready, and therefore extra careful with weapons, at all times.
2 Aiming high. Correct it by lots of practice sessions in the live-firing exercise area.
3 Leaving footprints and other signs when getting into position.
4 Misfires and stoppages due to dirty ammunition, magazines and weapons. Your life depends on keeping weapons in perfection condition at all times.
5 Everyone firing at the same target.
6 Bad fire control. The commander is unable to stop the assault and get the follow-up operation started immediately.
7 Opening fire too soon.
8 Poor observation, leading to the enemy arriving before anyone knew they were coming.

killing groups. How big they are, and how widely spread, will depend on the overall size of the attack force. These groups must be positioned so that they don't come under fire from friendly forces. This is especially important if the ambush is to take place at night or in bad visibility.

Some men should always be held in reserve. They should be stationed roughly half-way between the two stop groups, ready to reinforce any part of the ambush.

The look-out, posted along the track in the direction you expect the enemy to appear, is there not only to warn of the first approach, but to watch for stragglers and possible reinforcements as well. But always expect the unexpected. You may be 24 hours too late, for example, and catch the enemy coming back instead of going. Cover all possible directions of approach. When you are not sure which way the enemy is coming, dogs can be used to give early warning of their approach. But you must be sure that the dogs don't give your position away before time.

Just like any other sort of trap, an ambush has a sensitive trigger to spring it. It can be the lead terrorist reaching a pre-arranged position, for example, or a signal from the commander, or a chosen fire group opening up.

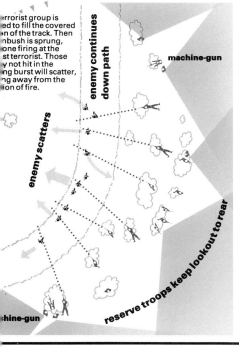

terrorist group is ...ed to fill the covered ...n of the track. Then ...mbush is sprung, ...one firing at the ...st terrorist. Those ...y not hit in the ...ng burst will scatter, ...ng away from the ...ion of fire.

enemy continues down path

machine-gun

enemy scatters

reserve troops keep lookout to rear

machine-gun

machine-gun

machine-gunners stop enemy escaping from killing ground

Commander

reserve troops

machine-gun

As the terrorists scatter they become difficult targets, but if they run directly away from the nearest gun they actually run into an increasing concentration of fire. Someone reaching the tree landmark would be in the line of fire of every gun in the ambush group.

each other, and not allowed to talk or communicate in any way. Don't try to interrogate them; leave that to trained intelligence officers. You may give away more information than you get, and you'll almost certainly put the prisoner on his guard. Prisoners should be thoroughly searched, and immobilised, but not treated brutally. Don't allow them to smoke, but do give them a minimum of food and water.

Casualties must be evacuated quickly, and the best way to do that is by vehicle or, better still, helicopters. The casevac force should be waiting in a secure location, and available at short notice.

The heat of the moment

An ambush is like a gun with a hair-trigger, loaded and cocked and with the safety off. Accidents happen quite frequently, because every member of the party is keyed up, waiting for the enemy force to arrive. Any movement can be enough to set off the fire-fight, and no-one will stop to think about whom he's shooting at. This is why it is so important to keep friendly forces out of the ambush area once the team is in position.

Below: A vital part of the security forces, the Bushmen of South West Africa are famous for their skills in bush warfare. The combination of their ancient skills with modern weapons and training produces some first-class fighting men able to beat the enemy at his own game.

Combat Report
Mauritius
Gang Riots in Plaine Verte

In January 1968 I was on loan from the British Army to the island of Mauritius in the Indian Ocean, commanding their little army, the Special Mobile Force.

I had been in Mauritius for a year, dealing with riots and urban terrorism as the country approached Independence. My force was small and not very well equipped, but I had managed to convince the government that I needed more soldiers and modern equipment. The increase in troops was taking place and recruits had started training, but the equipment was on its way by sea. Big trouble was brewing, and it was obvious that we wouldn't have our reinforcements in time.

Then it happened. The fear generated by fighting between criminal gangs was such that the whole of the Port Louis Muslim and Creole populations began to attack each other ferociously.

A State of Emergency

I received a report early on the morning of 21 January informing me that the riots had started the previous night and were still going on. I was to standby my unit and get myself down to Port Louis to attend a very important conference with the Governor, Chief Secretary, Prime Minister and Commissioner of Police. There were grim faces at this meeting as we were given details of the dead and injured, the destruction and the large numbers of refugees streaming into the police headquarters.

The Prime Minister wanted to declare an immediate State of Emergency, but with Independence due in a matter of weeks

The Commander of the Special Mobile Force in Mauritius where a British garrison was stationed.

everyone advised him against this. But he was a tough old bird, and wasn't to be thwarted. He turned to me and said, "Colonel, I want you to go out there, assess the situation and report back as soon as you can."

I hurried out to my Land Rover, managing as I went to waylay a truckload of police riot unit men for added protection. I told them to take me to the worst area, so we headed for the Muslim sector. As we approached I was amazed to see that even the smallest roads had roadblocks, and at each block were groups of armed youths. As we got closer, about eight men ran forward from a nearby roadblock and began hurling things at us. I thought they were rocks until they burst into flame, then I realised they were petrol bombs. Fortunately none actually struck the Land Rover.

By this time Corporal Prayag, my stalwart escort, was firing. He hit one man, who fell but got up and staggered away as the remainder of the gang ran off. As they fled I jumped from the cab and sped them on their way with my riot gun. By now I reckoned that I had enough information to give a general report, and so returned to Line Barracks.

I entered the conference room, still carrying my riot gun, and said to the Prime Minister, "Sir, it's complete anarchy out there at the moment!" The PM replied, "Very well, I'll declare a State of Emergency. I hope, Colonel, that our men will be able to deal with this?" I had to be honest. "Yes, sir, I'm sure we can, but you must understand that we shall have to kill some people." I wished I felt as confident as I sounded. The small number of troops was going to make it a tough task.

My soldiers were beginning to arrive in Line Barracks, and my staff had set up a tactical headquarters in an office vacated by the police.

Picking up the pieces after the inter-communal riots had been quelled by the fire action of the Special Mobile Force.

I pondered over an operational map of the city. The Moslem Plaine Verte area, where I had come from, was about the worst, and the police station there was coming under siege. I despatched a platoon there, then, as the rest of my men arrived, I sent them off to the various trouble spots.

Reports soon came in from the Plaine Verte police station that the platoon there was being fiercely attacked by large gangs using petrol bombs, rocks, and acid bombs made from electric light bulbs filled with sulphuric acid. So far one policeman had been wounded.

"That's him all right!"

With commendable discipline, and using minimum force, the platoon opened fire. They killed and wounded several attackers and dispersed them all. My other sub-units also had successes, slowly gaining the upper hand.

The refugees were pathetic. Hundreds of them, clutching a few precious belongings, poured into the fort. With limited water and virtually no sanitary facilities, the area soon became unsavoury.

I intended to spend the night at my Tactical HQ, but just before dusk the authorities became very agitated about a gang leader who'd reportedly been killed. He had personally murdered several people that day, and was feared throughout the city. Nobody knew if the report was true, so I was asked to send a patrol to Port Louis Hospital to investigate. With my soldiers fully extended I was not prepared to pull any of them off operations, so, taking with me a Mauritian officer who knew the gang leader by sight, I went myself.

The hospital corridor looked like a slaughterhouse. It was littered with people lying on stretchers or on the floor. Most wore dirty, makeshift bandages. The floor was streaked and splotched with blood, and harassed hospital staff hurried to and fro.

Eventually Sarge and I found the mortuary. Six bodies lay on tables.

"That's him all right!" said Sarge, pointing to one of the badly mutilated corpses.

Then I went back to my Tactical HQ for the night. By dusk, things were much quieter. As the debris glowed on the burned-out buildings and the dead and wounded were collected, we knew we had gained the initiative. We never lost this, and eventually gained complete control of the situation. But none of us would ever forget that first dreadful, dangerous day when things hung so precariously in the balance.

BUSH TRACKING AND COUNTERTRACKING

Trooper Reed, at point position on the patrol, was kneeling by the side of a cross-track in the thick woodland when the platoon commander caught up with him. He barred the way with a stick to stop the young lieutenant stumbling all over the 'spoor' (track), then pointed with the stick. "Four of them. Early yesterday, by the look of it; there are animal tracks coming and going over the top. Three wearing plain-soled boots and the other with car-tyre sandals on. I've seen his tracks before. He was part of that band that got away from B Platoon two weeks ago."

"Well, what are we waiting around for?" asked the lieutenant, and started off up the track.

Reed began to laugh.

"What the hell's so funny?"

"You're going the wrong way. The bastards had their boots tied on backwards."

The South African Defence Forces use airborne surveillance and intelligence to gather information about the movement of terrorist bands, but they often have to fall back on the oldest of all hunting skills — those of the tracker.

You don't have to be born to it to be a good tracker. This section, based on the SADF Anti-Terrorist Operations Manual, sets out how to find tracks, read them, and follow them in an effort to come to grips with insurgents.

Common sense and careful observation

The operation usually starts with two trackers going off to left and right along a base line, and then making a wide circle around the area. When they find the track, their first action is to keep everyone else well away from it — too much information can be lost by friendly forces trampling all over vital signs.

The trackers try to estimate the

5 points for successful tracking

1 Don't move so quickly that you overlook telltale signs.
2 Learn to use your sense of smell as well as your sight and hearing.
3 Don't just observe the tracks: interpret what they mean.
4 Get to know your enemy: study the terrorists' operating procedures, habits and equipment.
5 Be persistent: don't lose the will to win when you've lost the trail. Try to find it again.

Tracking demands intense concentration and an eye for detail. You have to be able to travel through the bush for days, lightly equipped and moving as fast as you can to catch up with the terrorists.

COUNTING THE TERRORISTS

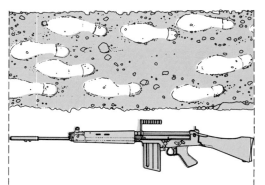

You can estimate how many people are in the group you are tracking by marking out a rectangle on the track. This should be as long as your rifle, and 45 cm wide. Count the number of footprints that fall completely into the area.

★ If the number is 4 or less, that is how many people you are following.

★ If the number is 5 or 6, add 2 and report 7 or 8.

This safety margin seems to work in most cases.

FOLLOWING THE SPOOR

The best unit for tracking is a four-man stick which is used to working together. Each takes turns to track and operate on the flank, communicating using hand signals in case the terrorists are closer than you think. If you think you can determine a consistent pattern in the movement of the terrorists you may be able to predict where they are heading and arrange an ambush.

number of terrorists, the age of the spoor, and the direction they've taken. These details are relayed back to central headquarters so that it can be used with information from other sources, and so widen the overall intelligence picture.

The man who first found the track will lead the hunt that follows, and he won't give up that position until he loses the trail. Then the casting-about operation will begin again until contact is re-established, and a new lead tracker takes over.

Trackers work in pairs whever they can – but in silence. This is a very vulnerable operation that could easily be the subject of an ambush. Talking and smoking are not allowed, and noise must always be kept to a minimum.

The signs that a tracker looks for – footprints and broken or disturbed vegetation are the most important – tell him the direction the quarry took, their numbers, how long ago they pas-

Interpreting the trail
The footprints should enable you to determine the direction and speed of the terrorists; how many are in the group; whether any of them are carrying heavy equipment; how many are men and how many women; and whether they know they are being followed.

Camouflage
If the terrorists suspect that they are being tracked they will probably try to disguise their trail. Walking backwards, brushing out their tracks behind them or moving over rocky ground or streams are the standard techniques.

Litter
Watch out for chewing-gum wrappers, cigarette ends, human faeces etc. A poorly-trained group of terrorists may leave all sorts of rubbish along their trail. Weather affects litter and can help you tell when the item was dropped: ration cans will go rusty, rain turns paper into pulp, and winds blow lighter objects away from the trail.

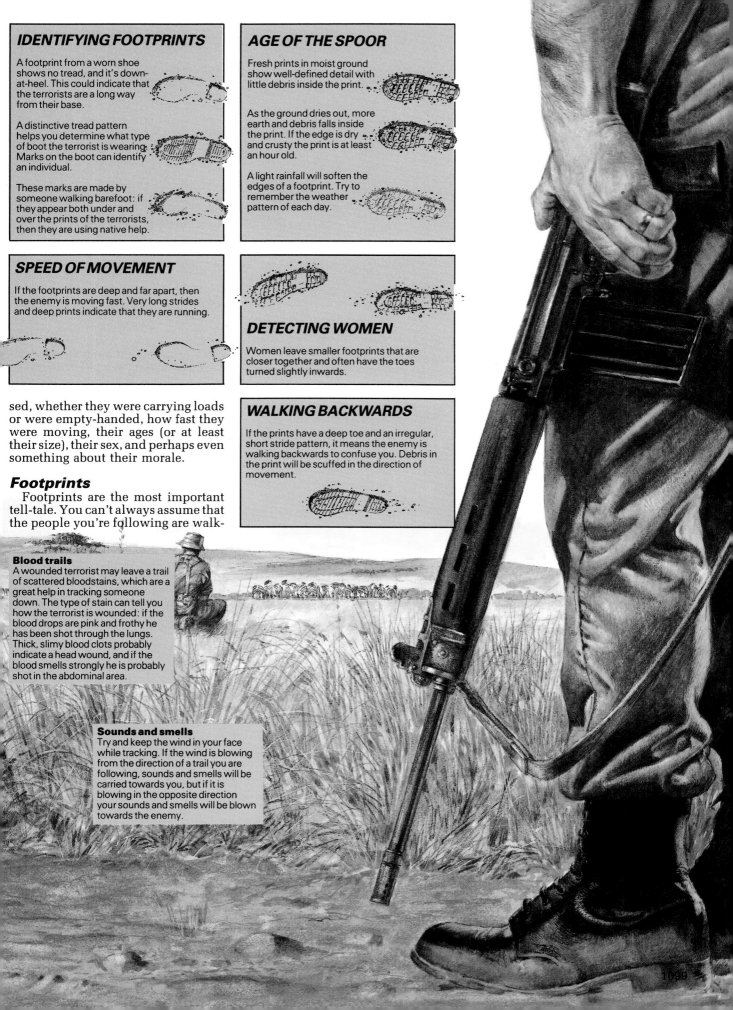

IDENTIFYING FOOTPRINTS

A footprint from a worn shoe shows no tread, and it's down-at-heel. This could indicate that the terrorists are a long way from their base.

A distinctive tread pattern helps you determine what type of boot the terrorist is wearing. Marks on the boot can identify an individual.

These marks are made by someone walking barefoot: if they appear both under and over the prints of the terrorists, then they are using native help.

AGE OF THE SPOOR

Fresh prints in moist ground show well-defined detail with little debris inside the print.

As the ground dries out, more earth and debris falls inside the print. If the edge is dry and crusty the print is at least an hour old.

A light rainfall will soften the edges of a footprint. Try to remember the weather pattern of each day.

SPEED OF MOVEMENT

If the footprints are deep and far apart, then the enemy is moving fast. Very long strides and deep prints indicate that they are running.

DETECTING WOMEN

Women leave smaller footprints that are closer together and often have the toes turned slightly inwards.

sed, whether they were carrying loads or were empty-handed, how fast they were moving, their ages (or at least their size), their sex, and perhaps even something about their morale.

WALKING BACKWARDS

If the prints have a deep toe and an irregular, short stride pattern, it means the enemy is walking backwards to confuse you. Debris in the print will be scuffed in the direction of movement.

Footprints

Footprints are the most important tell-tale. You can't always assume that the people you're following are walk-

Blood trails
A wounded terrorist may leave a trail of scattered bloodstains, which are a great help in tracking someone down. The type of stain can tell you how the terrorist is wounded: if the blood drops are pink and frothy he has been shot through the lungs. Thick, slimy blood clots probably indicate a head wound, and if the blood smells strongly he is probably shot in the abdominal area.

Sounds and smells
Try and keep the wind in your face while tracking. If the wind is blowing from the direction of a trail you are following, sounds and smells will be carried towards you, but if it is blowing in the opposite direction your sounds and smells will be blown towards the enemy.

ing in the direction that the toes point – they could have their boots tied on backwards (even when they're barefoot, they may be walking backwards!). But you can tell their direction of travel by checking which part of the indentation is the deepest – the deepest part shows the direction of march. The depth of the indentations will tell you whether they were carrying heavy loads or not, and so will the length of their stride. Heavily-laden men take short paces.

The difference between the depths

It is almost impossible to move through the African bush without leaving signs. Record the different prints you find: it may help you identify who you are tracking.

at the front and back will give you an idea of their speed – a running man, for example, leaves a deep toe print but little or nothing at the heel.

How well you'll be able to gauge the age of tracks depends a lot on weather conditions and even the time of day. Tracks in muddy ground that have no water standing in them are very fresh; soon after they're made, water will

start to fall back into it.

If there has been recent rain, and you can see splatter marks inside the track marks, that's a sure sign that they date from before the rain.

If it's an animal track you're on, look for signs that animals have walked on top of the human trail you're following. Most animals move back and forth along these tracks, which usually lead from their daytime lairs to water holes, at night. If there is a double set of animal tracks, one in each direction, over the top of the human footprints, then they are at least a night old.

Disturbed vegetation

It's very difficult to move through the African bush without leaving signs. Bent and broken grass, twigs and other vegetation can tell you not only which way the enemy went, but also how long ago he passed. Bent and broken grass will stay green to start with, but will turn brown after a day or so. Harder vegetation will take longer to change colour. Bear in mind that full sunlight will speed up the process, and shade will slow it down. Rain will affect the time-scale too.

Beware of ambush

If a track that has been quite distinct suddenly becomes much more difficult to follow, without any particular reason such as a change in the nature of the ground, the most likely conclusion is that the enemy has become extra-careful and is preparing to go to ground, either in a lying-up place or perhaps in ambush.

If this happens, the strategy is to move in a wide circle around the area, stay downwind, and look for signs – the usual trail signs, but also human scent, the smoke from fires and cigarettes, and cooking smells. Listen hard, too, for the sound of weapons being prepared and other signs of an enemy presence.

Hard going

Many factors affect the efficiency of a tracking operation. The type of ground, the character of the country, the weather and the direction of the sun (well-defined shadows help the tracker considerably), the sort of shoes the quarry is wearing, how much other traffic there is in the area, and the alertness of the trackers, can all make the job more or less difficult.

A smart enemy will use all the features of the country he's crossing to make the tracker's job more difficult. Hard or rocky ground, streams and water courses, irregular habits, back-tracking, changing shoes, even swing-

TELL-TALE SIGNS OF ENEMY MOVEMENT

1 Grass pushed down shows the direction they were moving in. If they were moving after sunrise the dew will be disturbed.

2 Mud or clay trapped in the tread of someone's boot can be left behind on rocks.

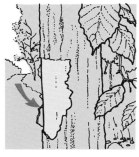

3 Watch trees and vines for scuff marks left by the terrorists.

4 A broken spider's web indicates recent movement through the area.

5 Look out for disturbed or overturned leaves that now have their damp underside exposed.

6 Similarly, overturned stones have their darker underside exposed.

ing from tree to tree ... These can all throw you off the scent. Be patient. If you lose the spoor, circle around and try to pick it up again. If that doesn't work, cast a wider circle. Look for things like broken spiders' webs; any sign that someone has passed by recently.

Look out for scavenging and food gathering

The enemy has to eat. If he's not been prepared for a long operation, he'll have to try to live off the land, or else beg, steal or buy food from people he encounters. Even if local inhabitants claim that food has been stolen from them, they could be lying to protect the terrorists. Don't follow their directions without checking independently.

Surer signs are fruit trees and edible plants that have been raided, disturbed bee hives, and traps and snares. Look out for discarded foodstuff – unripe fruit doesn't fall from trees of its own accord.

Insect clues

Look out for other signs, too, like recent fire sites, and urine and excrement – which you can often spot by a gathering of flies, yellow butterflies or dung beetles. The enemy may even be stupid enough to leave food wrappers lying about.

Look for freshly turned earth, and dig down to find out if anything has been buried. Remember to preserve material intact for examination, but

don't handle it with your bare fingers – it may have enemy prints on it.

The advantage is yours

Remember, above all, that the enemy is bound to leave some signs of his passage, no matter how small. Fresh scratches on rock and stones or logs overturned, tiny sprays of sand or loose dry earth, any signs of disturbance can give you valuable information. Covering his tracks will cost the enemy precious time, and he knows

Keep your head up and always try to look 20-30 metres ahead to follow the line of the trail. On rocky ground like this, look out for overturned rocks and scuff marks.

this. If you can press him hard, he's more likely to make mistakes, but if you're in hot pursuit you may miss them. Take some time. Examine all the signs carefully.

If you have dogs to help you, your job will be considerably easier. But that is the subject of a separate section on anti-terrorist tactics.

SEARCH PATTERNS AND FORMATIONS

A four-man tracker team moves with one man tracking, one man out to each side as a 'flanker', and the leader following along behind. If you are working ahead of friendly troops the tracker team leader is in charge of all men on the ground until you make contact. The flankers provide security for the tracker and must be ready for instant action: they must spot the terrorists first.

Cross grain method
If you lose the track, move laterally from the spoor left or right for 100 metres. Then double back to the original line of march. Before you turn, move forward 50-75 metres.

360° method
If the cross grain method fails, you must resort to walking in increasing circles until you pick up the trail again. Don't give up, some trackers have circled 5 km before finding it!

Y-shaped formation
The standard tracking formation is Y-shaped, with the flankers forming the open legs of the Y and the tracker at the junction, with the stick leader directly behind him. The stick leader remains about five metres behind the tracker, and the flankers remain forward of the tracker and to the side, subject to the terrain and vegetation.

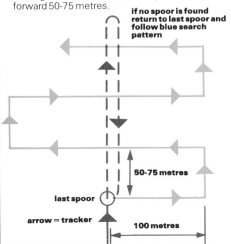

if no spoor is found return to last spoor and follow blue search pattern

50-75 metres

last spoor

arrow = tracker

100 metres

if no spoor is found return to last spoor and follow blue search pattern

last spoor

arrow = tracker

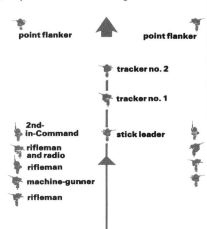

point flanker

point flanker

tracker no. 2

tracker no. 1

2nd-in-Command

stick leader

rifleman and radio

rifleman

machine-gunner

rifleman

Training the Battle Shot No. 1

NORMAL SAFETY PRECAUTIONS

Accurate rifle shooting remains the foundation of tactical success for the infantryman. Your ability as an accurate shot could make the difference between success and failure. For a lucky few, skill with small arms comes with uncanny ease but, for most of us, learning to become a competent shot requires dedication and hard work.

This series will teach you the basics of marksmanship and safe firearms handling, but remember that coaching can only take you so far. The rest depends on your determination to succeed. If you put the effort in, you will be rewarded, and you may well discover that shooting is an exciting and challenging sport as well as a vital military skill.

Before you do any live firing on the range, you must become familiar with your rifle: how it works, how it field-strips and cleans and, most importantly, how to handle it safely. It pays to know the history behind the gun: why it was developed and what the design is intended to do. This will help you understand its advantages and its limitations. Find out how the action operates – does it employ a piston like the SLR, or is the gas bled directly onto the bolt as on the M16?

Range safety

It is absolutely vital that you handle a firearm safely. Make it a matter of personal pride to be range safe. Practise your load, unload and make-safe drills until they are second nature. You cannot be too safe: better to make an apparently unnecessary check than accidentally shoot someone. ALWAYS ASSUME A WEAPON IS LOADED UNTIL YOU HAVE PROVED IT CLEAR.

The chamber of an L1A1 is inspected to show clear. The weapon will only be truly safe if the safety catch has been applied and the magazine removed, and if you have eyeballed the chamber and checked it clear. When handing someone a weapon, show them that it is clear and make sure they inspect the chamber for themselves and confirm it safe before taking it from you. They do this by saying 'clear'; only then should you release the bolt and fire off the action.

MAKING READY

The charging handle on an AR-15 is pulled back. Note that the shooter's forefinger is positioned correctly to the top of the trigger guard so as to minimise the possibility of a negligent discharge – the only time your finger should be inside the trigger guard is when you are in position and about to fire.

When on the firing point, keep your muzzle pointing in a safe direction at all times, i.e. downrange. When making any adjustments to your rifle, make sure you never muzzle-sweep someone else on the firing line. Never handle your weapon if there are people forward of the firing point.

Load and unload drills will differ slightly, depending on the rifle. Here a Galil is loaded with a standard 35-round magazine. The soldier has adopted the loading position and is holding the rifle by the pistol grip in the right hand. The forefinger is clear of the trigger guard and the muzzle is pointing downrange. The safety catch is set to 'safe'. The magazine is then inserted and made secure by putting the front of the magazine in first and then pulling back to make sure it has engaged the magazine catch. Then give it a quick rattle to make sure it won't come off.

To unload, check the safety is at 'safe'. Remove the magazine and pull back the cocking handle. Tilt the rifle to the right to eject any rounds downwards (pointing the muzzle downrange). Then allow the working parts forwards and recock; repeat this at least three times. Hold the working part to the rear and then check the chamber is clear of any rounds. Then let the working parts forwards, set the safety catch at 'rounds' and squeeze the trigger off, with the muzzle pointing downrange. You carry out this procedure, known as NSPs (normal safety precautions), every time you pick up a weapon, enter a building or vehicle, or hand a weapon over.

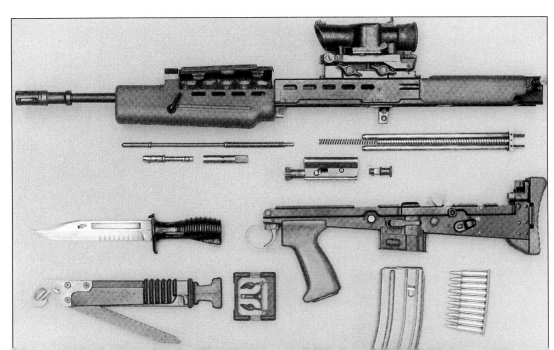

You must become familiar with your rifle, whether it is a sophisticated weapons system such as the SA80 (seen here stripped down to a mass of bits and pieces) or the now ancient but user-friendly AK-47. If you keep your rifle well maintained it will shoot with maximum reliability and accuracy. Good shooting is the co-ordination of many different elements, human and mechanical. It is essential that you have total confidence in your weapon: stripping and cleaning is a good way to get acquainted.

THE PRINCIPLES OF MARKSMANSHIP

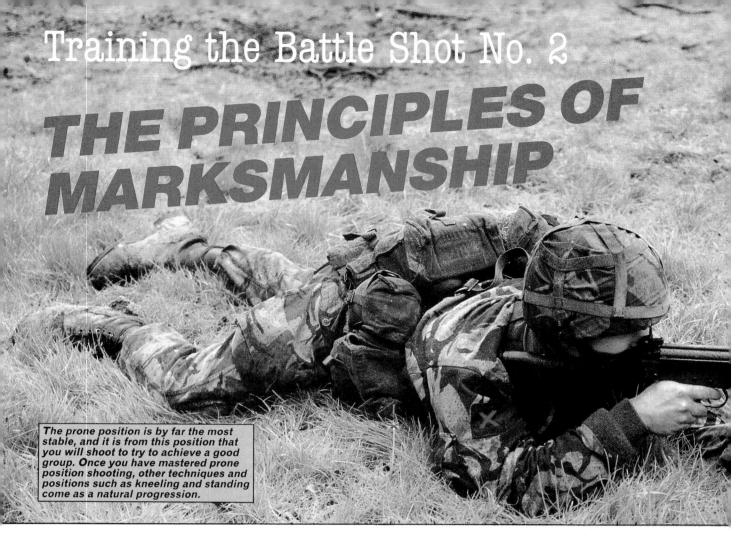

The prone position is by far the most stable, and it is from this position that you will shoot to try to achieve a good group. Once you have mastered prone position shooting, other techniques and positions such as kneeling and standing come as a natural progression.

Good shooting means constantly practising your skills until the shots you fire have the same point of impact on the target: this is known as grouping. Until you can shoot a reasonably tight group from the prone position, you won't be able to adjust (zero) the sights of your rifle properly. Before you can maintain the same firing position and point of aim each time a shot is fired, you will have to understand the principles of marksmanship.

This is not nearly as awesome as it sounds. Putting the principles into practice on the range demands maximum determination and concentration, but if you apply them correctly you will have the satisfaction of consistently achieving nice, tightly-shot groups.

The four principles

1. Your position and hold must be firm enough to support the rifle.
2. The rifle must point naturally at the target without any physical effort.
3. Sight alignment (aiming) must be correct.
4. The shot must be released and followed through without any disturbance to the position.

EYE RELIEF

Eye relief is the distance between the eye and your rear sight. This should be somewhere between 1½ and 2 inches or (in metric)) between 38 and 50mm. This distance is mainly determined by the size and shape of the rifle butt, and can be altered by modifying your position. Lying with the body straighter behind the rifle will increase eye relief; lying more at an angle causes it to decrease.

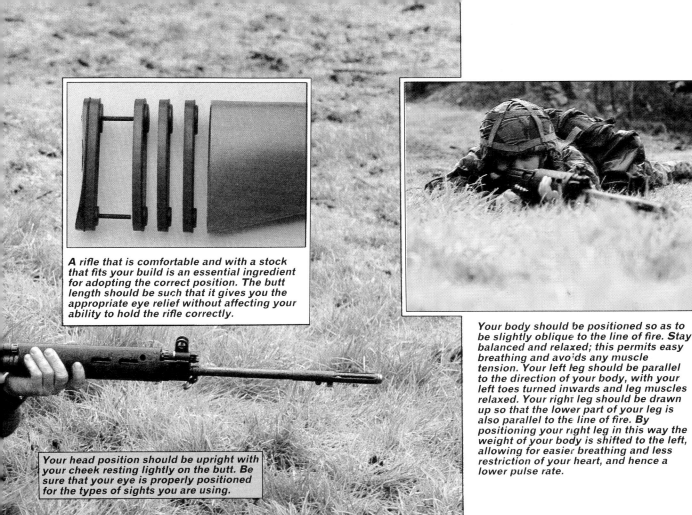

A rifle that is comfortable and with a stock that fits your build is an essential ingredient for adopting the correct position. The butt length should be such that it gives you the appropriate eye relief without affecting your ability to hold the rifle correctly.

Your head position should be upright with your cheek resting lightly on the butt. Be sure that your eye is properly positioned for the types of sights you are using.

Your body should be positioned so as to be slightly oblique to the line of fire. Stay balanced and relaxed; this permits easy breathing and avoids any muscle tension. Your left leg should be parallel to the direction of your body, with your left toes turned inwards and leg muscles relaxed. Your right leg should be drawn up so that the lower part of your leg is also parallel to the line of fire. By positioning your right leg in this way the weight of your body is shifted to the left, allowing for easier breathing and less restriction of your heart, and hence a lower pulse rate.

Stability

Stability of your position requires positive contact with the ground. Your rifle should be supported firmly by three points of your body: the left hand, right hand and chest. Your left elbow must be fairly close to the rifle so that the weight of the weapon is supported by the rear of your elbow joint bone. This should ensure that there is no undue muscular strain, which would create a variable factor in maintaining a correct position. The rifle handguard should lie across the palm of your hand and be held in a way that is firm enough to control the weapon without the need to grip tightly. Your right hand should be positioned high on the pistol grip. Your grip should be firm, pulling back into the shoulder and allowing the trigger finger to rest pointing parallel to the axis of the barrel. Having adopted the correct grip, your right elbow should now be positioned so as not to cause any twisting of the wrist. Remember that your right hand is controlling the weapon and must be in a correct position.

Clothing effect

Correct clothing is an often-neglected but important factor in developing an accurate shooting technique. This would soon become apparent if you attempted lying in the prone position for any length of time with a 4.98-kg rifle dressed in a t-shirt and bermuda shorts. A shirt, jumper and jacket will provide the necessary layers of clothing to protect your elbows and cushion your shoulder from recoil. Adequate clothing will also help you maintain a steady and comfortable position.

Natural pointing is the second of the marksmanship principles and is fairly self-explanatory. The rifle should point naturally towards the target without any physical effort. To achieve this, remember that the rifle itself is the key element of the firing position, so the alignment of the position determines the alignment of the rifle to the target. Any physical strain at the time of firing will result in the rifle being pulled by recoil out of this alignment, and will consequently result in the bullets fired being directed away from the point of aim. Adopting a position that naturally points the rifle at the target will eliminate any inconsistencies caused by muscle strain. As with all the other marksmanship principles, natural pointing is a case of 'practice makes perfect'.

Training the Battle Shot No. 3

SIGHT ALIGNMENT & FOLLOW THROUGH

To shoot a good, tight group from which you can accurately zero your rifle's sights, you must be free of any inconsistencies in the way you take each shot. Understanding the principles of marksmanship will help you attain this consistency.

We have already dealt with the first two principles; now you can learn to master sight alignment and follow-through.

Sight alignment

Sight alignment is the alignment of the eye with the centre of the backsight aperture and the central point of the foresight tip. Of course, with optical sights you have the advantage of just the one combined sight picture to concentrate on. All you have to do to obtain a correct sight picture is to place the properly-aligned sight onto your point of aim.

Misaligned sights will result in your shots impacting away from your point of aim, so it is essential that you concentrate on keeping the tip of your foresight centred in the rear sight aperture. Remember that it is not humanly possible for the eye to focus on the rear sight, foresight and target at the same time.

At the moment the shot is released, the foresight tip should be clearly in focus to ensure that you have your sights correctly aligned. With iron sights the relationship between the rearsight aperture and the foresight is critical. Any errors in this relationship will cause misplaced shots and will become greater in proportion to the distance from which you are firing. At 300 yards and over, any such errors will have fairly drastic results.

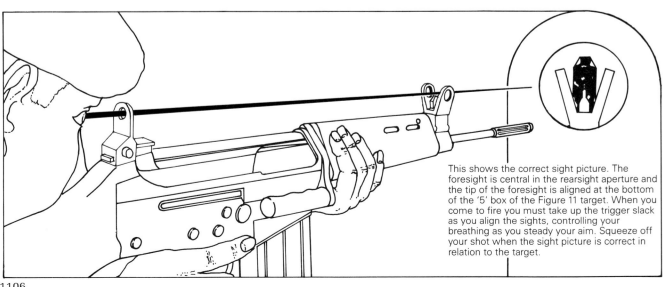

This shows the correct sight picture. The foresight is central in the rearsight aperture and the tip of the foresight is aligned at the bottom of the '5' box of the Figure 11 target. When you come to fire you must take up the trigger slack as you align the sights, controlling your breathing as you steady your aim. Squeeze off your shot when the sight picture is correct in relation to the target.

When aligning your sights remember the points from your first marksmanship principle relating to the positioning of the head on the butt to obtain correct eye relief. Consistent eye relief, the distance between the eye and the rear sight, is critical to a correct sight picture.

The final marksmanship principle, shot release and follow-through, is the combination of three actions: breathing, trigger operation and following the shot through. Although this seems like three separate skills they cannot be practised in isolation and will only be of real benefit when all three elements are employed as one integrated action.

This 'lollipop' device is used by an instructor to check that your sight picture is correct and to monitor your trigger operation. He can quickly detect whether you are snatching at the trigger instead of gently squeezing it off.

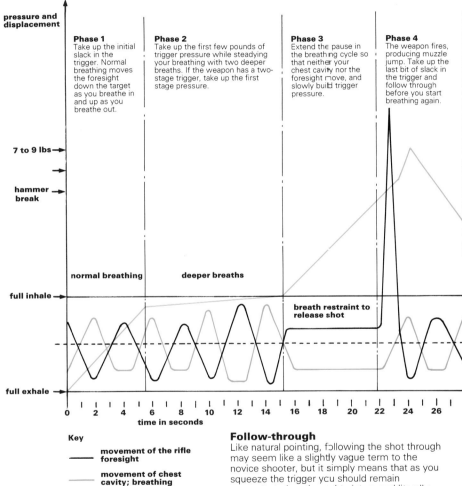

pressure and displacement

Phase 1
Take up the initial slack in the trigger. Normal breathing moves the foresight down the target as you breathe in and up as you breathe out.

Phase 2
Take up the first few pounds of trigger pressure while steadying your breathing with two deeper breaths. If the weapon has a two-stage trigger, take up the first stage pressure.

Phase 3
Extend the pause in the breathing cycle so that neither your chest cavity nor the foresight move, and slowly build trigger pressure.

Phase 4
The weapon fires, producing muzzle jump. Take up the last bit of slack in the trigger and follow through before you start breathing again.

7 to 9 lbs →

hammer break →

normal breathing   deeper breaths

full inhale →

breath restraint to release shot

full exhale →

0 2 4 6 8 10 12 14 16 18 20 22 24 26

time in seconds

Key

⎯⎯⎯ **movement of the rifle foresight**

⎯⎯⎯ **movement of chest cavity; breathing**

⎯⎯⎯ **trigger pressure**

Breath control
Breathing causes body movement, and when shooting it must therefore be controlled. When you breathe normally your lungs are neither completely filled nor emptied, and on breathing out there is a natural pause. This normal breathing cycle takes on average about five seconds. When shooting you need to extend this natural pause to six or seven seconds so as to be able to fire a shot with minimum body movement.

Once you are in position to fire you should try to develop a normal breathing cycle. When you are in the aim, take two deep breaths to oxygenate the body; this will assist your concentration during the breathing pause. In this six- or seven-second pause, squeeze off your shot.

Make sure that you do not extend the pause beyond at most seven seconds, as your body's natural impulse to resume normal breathing will impede your ability to concentrate properly.

Trigger operation
During the breathing pause you must be able to operate the trigger without disturbing your position. Make sure that the hold of your controlling hand is correctly positioned towards the top of the pistol grip; this will ensure that your trigger finger is correctly located. Before coming up to the aim, take off any slack pressure on the trigger. When you have a correct sight picture and want to take your shot, engage the trigger by a graduated squeezing action. Snatching the trigger will pull your shot off the point of aim. Be careful not to disturb your sight picture when you are increasing the pressure on the trigger prior to taking your shot. If your sight picture has altered during this process, try to keep the pressure on the trigger constant until you have realigned the sights.

Follow-through
Like natural pointing, following the shot through may seem like a slightly vague term to the novice shooter, but it simply means that as you squeeze the trigger you should remain concentrated on the sight picture and literally 'follow the shot through', ensuring that you do not alter your position in response to the trigger action and recoil, thus possibly disturbing the stability of your rifle while the bullet is still in the barrel. Of course, this would result in the shot being misplaced.

To attain a good follow-through, be sure that as your shot is fired you keep the trigger held to the rear. Your eye must remain open and you must watch for any movement of the foresight. Recoil will move the barrel in an upward direction, but if your position and hold are correct the sights should settle either on or close to your point of aim.

You are now armed with the principles of marksmanship. Make sure that you put them to good use when you come to the next stage, which will be grouping and zeroing.

On Target with the Tokarev

From the Smith & Wesson .44 Russian to the gas-seal Nagant of 1895, all Russian army pistols were of foreign design — but in the early 1920s the new Soviet Army demanded a locally designed, modern, automatic pistol instead of an archaic revolver. As a result of this demand two designs were put forward, both in 7.65 mm ACP calibre; then, the Artillery Commission (responsible for small arms design) demanded that the 7.63 mm Mauser cartridge should be the future standard pistol round. The power of this cartridge was such that it wiped out both the contestants on the spot, since neither could be adapted to take the new cartridge.

Cossack to the rescue

In 1929 a new designer appeared, Fedor Tokarev. He had spent his apprenticeship with a village blacksmith in the 1880s, then went to a Military Trade School to qualify as an armourer. He became an NCO in the Cossacks, returned to the Trade School as instructor, and by the time the 1914-18 war began was an officer, working on designs for an automatic rifle. In spite of his commissioned rank he survived the bloodier aspects of the Revolution to become Assistant Director for Inspection and Manufacture at the Sestoresk arms factory.

Now he stepped forward with a design for a 7.62 mm service automatic, one based on John Moses Browning's 'swinging link' method of breech locking used in the US Army's Colt M1911 pistol. In this system the barrel is attached to the pistol frame by link hinges at both ends. The top of the barrel carries ribs that engage in grooves in the underside of the slide.

With the slide forward and the breech closed, the lugs and grooves are engaged.

When the pistol is fired, the slide moves rearward due to the recoil and, because of the engaged lugs, takes the barrel with it. But the moving barrel is made to pivot, because the lower end of the link is pinned to the frame. As a result, after a short period of locked recoil, the barrel comes free of the slide, which continues rearwards while the barrel is stopped. The slide goes back, compressing a return spring and cocking the hammer, then goes forward under spring pressure to load a fresh round into the chamber and push the barrel forward, lifting it above the link pivot so that the lugs engage once more into the slide.

So far so good, but not very original.

A child in an Afghan refugee camp shows off a Tokarev pistol acquired from the Afghan army. Remember Kipling's 'arithmetic on the frontier': a 10-rupee rifle or an old Russian pistol in the hands of a boy can kill you as surely as the latest rifle. The Soviet withdrawal will leave Afghanistan with one of the most heavily-armed populations outside the Middle East.

Left: The Tokarev 7.62-mm pistol was the first military handgun to be designed and produced in the USSR. First issued in the 1930s, it is believed that over 90,000 were made before production ceased in 1954. It has been supplied to Soviet allies and guerrilla forces all over the world and will still be encountered for many years to come.

Right: One of the most famous Soviet wartime photographs shows a Red Army officer leading the way with a Tokarev. The Nagant gas-seal revolvers it replaced could have most of their problems cured by a hammer, and the TT-33 was similarly built for strength and reliability. There is no safety catch or grip safety.

(And remember that by this time the Browning GP35 had been perfected, and had gone beyond the swinging link to use a fixed lug.) But Tokarev had aimed his design at the practical soldier.

For example, he designed the hammer and lockwork in a single removable module, so that the entire mechanism could be slipped out of the frame very easily for cleaning or repair. He appreciated that the weakest spot on any automatic weapon is the feed system, and particularly the magazine lips. So, the lips on his magazine were rudimentary, and the actual feed guide was machined into the steel of the frame, where it was unlikely to wear or be damaged. Minor damage to the actual magazine lips didn't matter much, and rough repair was quite sufficient to allow the weapon to work well.

No safety

Another feature was the complete absence of any sort of safety catch or grip safety. Tokarev appears to have argued that revolvers did not usually have safety catches, and that proper training would ensure the weapons were used properly. Moreover, when pistols are needed, they are usually needed in a hurry, with no time to think about safety catches. It is interesting to see that similar thinking in

the 1970s led to a number of modern designs without manual safety devices, though in these some fairly complex automatic safeties have been incorporated.

It would be as well here to explain why the Artillery Commission's demand for a 7.63mm Mauser chambered pistol became translated into a 7.62mm design. In fact there was no difference; 7.62mm was the standard Soviet rifle calibre, and the

South African forces in pursuit of SWAPO guerrillas carry captured Soviet weapons. The man on the right has a Tokarev TT-33 in his holster. To his front lies an AK fitted with the 100-round drum magazine of the RPD light machine-gun.

7.63mm Mauser bullet worked perfectly adequately in the Soviet 7.62mm rifling. So the cartridge was re-christened 7.62mm to avoid problems over nomenclature and as the '7.62mm Patron Obrazets 1930g' remained the Soviet pistol and submachine-gun round until the 1960s. And having 7.62mm as the common pistol, rifle, submachine-gun and machine-gun calibre certainly reduced manufacturing problems in the barrel-making factories.

Tokarev's design sailed through the usual tests with flying colours, and in December 1930 manufacture of 1,000 Tula-Tokarev 30 (TT-30) pistols was authorised for troop trials. These took

Inside the Tokarev

place in 1931/32 and approval was given for adoption into service. At the same time, however, some suggestions for modifications to simplify manufacture were put forward.

The TT-30 had a removable backstrap on the butt, to simplify fitting and repairing the trigger spring; this was changed so that the entire butt formed a solid portion of the frame, the trigger spring problem being considered less important than solid design. The most significant change suggested was to do away with milling out the two lugs on top of the barrel and, instead, machine two complete rings around the barrel, the top sections of which acted as the lugs. This made no difference to the pistol's operation, but made manufacture much quicker, since the rings could be machined on the lathe as the exterior of the barrel was being turned, instead of being cut by a separate machine in a separate manufacturing step.

These changes were adopted and the design now became the TT-33 pistol; it went into production in 1936. It has been estimated that about 93,000 TT-30s were made before the TT-33 went into service. It is believed to have stayed in production in Russia until 1954.

The TT-33's variants

As is usual with their weapons the Soviets exported countless thousands of Tokarev pistols and authorized manufacture by their satellites, so that there are several minor variations on the TT-33 design. There are the Chinese Type 54, the Polish TT, the Hungarian M48, the North Korean Type 68 and the Yugoslavian M57, all of which are simply locally-made Tokarevs. Distinguishing them is largely a matter of examining the markings, though there are some points of note. The Chinese Type 54 has the grooves on the rear of the slide (in order to grip it for cocking) entirely narrow, whereas the original Soviet model, and the Polish copies, use alternate broad and narrow grooves. The Hungarian M48 also has narrow grooves and can be further identified by the badge moulded into the grips — a star, wheatsheaf and hammer surrounded by a wreath. The Korean Type 68 has the slide grooves narrow but sloping forward; internally, the swinging link has been abandoned and replaced by a fixed lug with a cam path, similar to that used in the Browning GP35, and it has the magazine release positioned at the heel of the butt instead of using a push-button behind the trigger guard as do all the

The Tokarev is based on the Browning automatic pistol design with modifications to the lock mechanism and the magazine. There is no safety catch or grip safety, the designer apparently believing that the Soviet Army did not need any since the revolvers the Tokarev replaced had no safety either. Compare this cutaway with that of the Colt M1911.

Foresight

The accuracy of the Tokarev depends largely on your choice of ammunition. Shooting the Soviet 7.62-mm M30 cartridge, it comes back into the aim quite quickly. Tokarevs can usually accept 7.63-mm Mauser, but this tends to produce too much recoil for an accurate double-tap.

Field stripping the Tokarev

1 Press the magazine catch on the left-hand side of the butt and remove the magazine.

2 Rack back the slide and check the chamber is clear.

6 Remove the recoil spring and guide from the front of the slide.

7 Then turn the barrel bushing to the right to unlock the barrel.

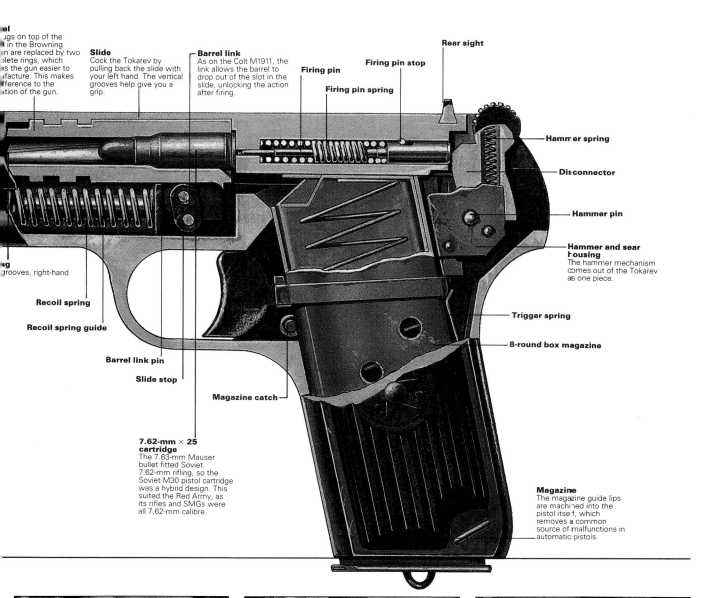

el
ugs on top of the
... in the Browning
...n are replaced by two
...lete rings, which
...s the gun easier to
...ufacture. This makes
...ference to the
...tion of the gun.

Slide
Cock the Tokarev by
pulling back the slide with
your left hand. The vertical
grooves help give you a
grip.

Barrel link
As on the Colt M1911, the
link allows the barrel to
drop out of the slot in the
slide, unlocking the action
after firing.

Rear sight

Firing pin

Firing pin stop

Firing pin spring

Hammer spring

Disconnector

Hammer pin

Hammer and sear housing
The hammer mechanism
comes out of the Tokarev
as one piece.

g
grooves, right-hand

Recoil spring

Recoil spring guide

Barrel link pin

Slide stop

Magazine catch

Trigger spring

8-round box magazine

7.62-mm × 25 cartridge
The 7.63-mm Mauser
bullet fitted Soviet
7.62-mm rifling, so the
Soviet M30 pistol cartridge
was a hybrid design. This
suited the Red Army, as
its rifles and SMGs were
all 7.62-mm calibre.

Magazine
The magazine guide lips
are machined into the
pistol itself, which
removes a common
source of malfunctions in
automatic pistols.

3 The slide stop barrel locking pin is located on the right side of the receiver.

4 Remove the locking pin from the left.

5 Now pull the barrel assembly and slide forward out of the guides in the receiver.

8 Remove the barrel and barrel bushing from the slide forwards.

9 Lift the hammer mechanism out of the receiver.

10 Completed field strip. You can also strip it like a Colt .45 as shown in Issue 20.

The Tokagypt 58 is a version of the Tokarev used by the Eygptian army. Manufactured in Hungary, it has a safety catch and a better, one-piece, plastic grip. Most importantly it is chambered for 9-mm Parabellum, which is a profound improvement on the Soviet 7.62-mm round.

others. The Yugoslavian M57 also has forward-sloping grooves on the slide.

The only major variations, and perhaps the most practical designs of all, were the Hungarian-made 'Tokagypt' and the Yugoslavian M70(d), both of which were the TT-33 redesigned into 9 mm Parabellum calibre. The Tokagypt was developed for the Egyptian Army, but strangely it did not go down well with them and most of these sensible pistols finished in the hands of Egyptian police and security forces.

The Yugoslavian M70(d) appears to have been developed for the export market but, again, nobody seems to have taken it up in any numbers. It is likely that countries outside the

Battlefield Evaluation: comparing

Tokarev TT-33

When evaluating the Tokarev you can easily finish up comparing eggs with bananas. It would be quite wrong to compare the TT-33 with, say, the SIG P-230: they belong to different generations and were designed with different ends in view. The following evaluation matches the Tokarev against its contemporaries. Some have stood the test of time and others have vanished into obscurity.

Specification:
Cartridge: 7.62-mm×25 Tokarev
Weight: 0.85 kg unloaded
Length: 195mm
Barrel length: 116mm
Magazine: 8-round box

Assessment
Reliability ★★★★
Accuracy ★★★
Age ★★★★
Worldwide users ★★

The Tokarev is now in the hands of guerrilla forces all over the world, and may crop up anywhere.

Radom wz 35

Developed in 1935, just as the TT-33 was perfected, the Polish Radom ranks as one of the best 9-mm combat pistols of all time. Firing 9-mm Parabellum, it has better stopping power than the Tokarev. Somewhat heavy, it soaks up the recoil and is pleasant and accurate to fire. It uses the same type of locking cam as the GP35 and has a safety catch that lowers the hammer on to a locked firing pin so that it can be quickly thumb-cocked for firing.

Specification:
Cartridge: 9-mm Parabellum
Weight: 1.02kg loaded
Length: 197mm
Barrel length: 121mm
Magazine: 8-round box

Assessment
Reliability ★★★★
Accuracy ★★★★
Age ★★★
Worldwide users ★

Developed in Poland, the Radom was a contemporary of the TT-30 and was a far superior weapon.

Walther P38

This faced the Tokarev on the Eastern Front from 1941 to 1945 and it remains in production and service to this day. Perhaps its advantage lies in the barrel design. Since the P-38 barrel doesn't tip, it is inherently more accurate than the TT-33. The shape of the butt also makes it more comfortable to shoot, but as combat weapons there is not much to choose between them.

Specification:
Cartridge: 9-mm Parabellum
Weight: 0.96kg loaded
Length: 219mm
Barrel length: 124mm
Magazine: 8-round box

Assessment
Reliability ★★★★
Accuracy ★★★★
Age ★★★
Worldwide users ★★

The P38 replaced the Luger as the German service pistol in 1940. It has far outlasted the Tokarev.

Soviet Bloc, to which these pistols may have been offered for sale, preferred to adopt more modern 9mm Parabellum designs instead of the somewhat elderly Tokarev.

Elderly it may be, but as a practical combat pistol there is not much wrong with the TT-33. The 7.62 mm Mauser cartridge has a high velocity and good penetrating power, while the weight of bullet is not such as to cause excessive recoil, so that it is possible to fire accurately and get back into the aim quite quickly. The simplicity and strength of the design you can take for granted – the Soviets would not have kept it in production for nearly 25 years unless it had those features.

The basis of the Tokarev design is the Colt 1911, but it has not lasted as well. The Red Army had good reason to pick the 7.62-mm cartridge, but this decision ensured the TT-33 would have limited appeal outside the USSR.

the Tokarev with its rivals

Lahti M35

Another design that came face-to-face with the Tokarev in the 1939-45 years, the Lahti is an elegant 9-mm design from Finland. It looks like a Luger but has a totally different mechanism. Renowned as the one pistol that never jams under conditions of extreme cold, it is retained in service by the Finnish army and in Sweden largely for this reason. It is highly accurate and a lovely pistol to shoot, but a great deal more expensive than the Tokarev.

Specification:
Cartridge: 9-mm Parabellum
Weight: 1.22 kg unloaded
Length: 245mm
Barrel length: 105mm
Magazine: 8-round box

Assessment
Reliability   *****
Accuracy   ****
Age   ****
Worldwide users **

The Lahti is retained for its cold weather tolerance, although speed reloading is an acquired art.

CZ 38

This Czech design was a contemporary of the Tokarev and can be cited as how to get it wrong. It is 9-mm calibre but is actually a blowback using the 9-mm Short cartridge, so its stopping power is nowhere near as good as the TT-33 or any other weapon shown here. The trigger mechanism only allowed self-cocking and had a stiff pull. Fortunately the Czechs were so late developing it that their army hardly saw it. All the wartime production was taken by the Germans, which served them right.

Specification:
Cartridge: 9-mm Short
Weight: 0.94kg unloaded
Length: 206mm
Barrel length: 118mm
Magazine: 8-round box

Assessment
Reliability   ***
Accuracy   *
Age   ****
Worldwide users *

Manufactured to a high standard, the CZ 38 was a clumsy and inaccurate weapon inferior to the Tokarev.

SACM Mle 35A

The French army's service automatic, adopted in 1935, was a sound design, ruined by a bad choice of cartridge. Based on the Browning swinging link, it used a removeable hammer module like the Tokarev. It had a slide-mounted safety and a magazine safety which (as on the Browning GP35) prevented firing if the magazine was out. But the weak 7.65-mm Longue cartridge was underpowered and of little combat value. After the war they redesigned the gun to take 9-mm Parabellum, which turned it into a reasonable weapon.

Specification:
Cartridge: 7.65-mm Longue
Weight: 0.73kg unloaded
Length: 189mm
Barrel length: 109mm
Magazine: 8-round box

Assessment
Reliability   ***
Accuracy   ***
Age   ****
Worldwide users *

Like the TT-33, the Mle 35 was handicapped by the choice of cartridge, but a switch to 9-mm made all the difference.

Soviet Amphibian: the PT-76 light tank

Right and below:
The Soviet army
developed the PT-76
to equip their recce
units with a light
tank that could cross
rivers without delay.
It still serves with
their Naval Infantry
as a Main Battle
Tank.

The PT-76 amphibious light tank is without doubt the world's most successful reconnaissance vehicle to see service since World War II. Built at the Volgagrad Tank Plant in the southern USSR, it first entered service in 1951 and is still in limited service with the Soviet Naval Infantry. It can be found throughout the Warsaw Pact and has been exported to many Third World countries. It has seen combat in Africa, the Middle East and Far East.

Developed from the Pinguin cross-country vehicle, the PT-76 was designed to fulfil the dual roles of reconnaissance vehicle and light tank. During its advance through Poland and Eastern Germany in 1944 and 1945 the Red Army had sorely lacked a vehicle that was not only powerful enough to engage the German armoured screen but also agile enough to traverse marshy and water-logged terrain. Work began on two new scout vehicles in 1944, but it took seven years before the design of the PT-76 was approved.

Amphibious capabilities

In order to be buoyant, the PT-76 is unusually large for so lightly armed a vehicle. Fully amphibious, it is propelled through the water with the help of two water jets at the rear of the hull. Before the tank enters the water, a trim vane – stored on the glacis plate when not in use – is erected at the front of the hull, to give the driver a degree of protection. At the same time, two electric bilge pumps are switched on. There is a third, manual bilge pump on board, in case these prove inadequate. A schnorkel can be fitted in case the rear decking becomes awash, preventing the engine from drawing air through the normal louvres. The PT-76 cannot operate in rivers or cross tides faster than 8 km/h (5 mph) however, so it is virtually useless in rough weather.

Design

Despite its size (larger than many small tanks) the PT-76's slab-sided, all-welded hull offers only minimum protection – its armour is nowhere more than 14-mm thick. This is sufficient to stop small arms fire, but artillery shrapnel or a direct hit from the 30-mm Rarden cannon or 25-mm Hughes Chain Gun fitted to British and US armoured cars would prove lethal.

The driver, seated at the front of the hull, is provided with a circular hatch cover that swings to the right. The commander and gunner sit in the small "frying pan" turret in the centre of the hull. The commander, to the right of the gunner, is also responsible for loading the 76-mm gun – which

Right: A joint East German/Soviet amphibious exercise in the Baltic. In a future European war, PT-76s would spearhead the Warsaw Pact assault on Denmark.

The PT-76 is difficult to steer in the water and choppy water can easily drown the engine if not the crew. The schnorkel is only partly successful.

Coming ashore: the PT-76 was intended more for river crossing than beach assault. It copes very well with marshy terrain.

Inside the PT-76

Coming soon to a beach near you: the PT-76 may be old, but it is the only amphibious tank in Soviet service. Any attack in central Europe would see the PT-76s of Soviet Naval Infantry splashing ashore on the Danish coast and operating against the northern flank of NATO forces in Germany. The low military value of this tank could be counter-balanced by the surprise factor of its appearance *en masse* before the defending troops were properly deployed.

Exerting a ground pressure of just 0.479 kg/cm², the PT-76 performs well over snow. This PT-76 has its snorkel raised in readiness for a river crossing.

D-56T 76.2-mm gun
Based on the Red Army's World War II tank gun, the D-56 fires APHE, Frag-HE, HEAT and HVAP ammunition but the sights are only marked for the first two. Firing HEAT or HVAP the gunner has to rely on a firing table or take a guess. The PT-76 could only knock out a well-protected NATO tank when shooting from the rear within 500m. Not easy!

Central driver's periscope
The driver has three periscopes. This one can be raised for him to see over the trim vane when the vehicle is in the water. Unfortunately, it does not give a good enough view.

Soviet naval insignia

Front hull armour
The glacis is protected by just 11mm of armour sloped at 80 degrees. This will keep out rifle rounds and most heavy machine-gun fire, but nothing else.

Driver
When the vehicle is in the water, you cannot see much from the driver's position and you have to rely largely on steering instructions from the vehicle commander. Unlike most Western tanks there is no bulkhead separating the driver from the other crew members.

makes his job very difficult. The two turret crewmen share a single hatch cover that hinges forward.

Although a ventilation system is fitted at the rear of the turret, there is no NBC (Nuclear, Biological and Chemical) filtration system. Thus, the crew is forced to operate in hot, cumbersome protective suits. An infra-red driving light can be fitted, and a white searchlight is fitted as standard. Navigation lights can be fitted for swimming. The PT-76 can also lay its own smoke screen with the aid of diesel fuel injected into the exhaust.

Powerpack

The Model V-6, 6-cylinder in-line water-cooled diesel engine at the rear of the hull is in effect a half-sized version of the engine in the elderly T-54 main battle tank. Developing 240 bhp at 1,800 rpm, it can power the 14-tonne vehicle at up to 44 km/h (27.5 mph) along roads and 10 km/h (6.25 mph) in the water, to a range of 260 km. Extra range comes from additional fuel tanks, fitted above the engine housing when required.

Firepower

Early model PT-76s were fitted with the 76.2-mm D-56 T gun, a development of the T-34/76 armament that proved so successful during the closing stages of World War II. Equipped with a semi-automatic vertical sliding wedge breech block, hydro-pneumatic recuperator and hydraulic buffer, the gun is theoretically capable of a maximum rate of fire of 15 rpm. But given the lack of sophisticated targeting equipment and the dual role of the commander/loader, a rate of 6 to 8 rpm would seem more realistic. Elevation, from +30° to −4°, is manual and therefore slow. Traverse through 360° is powered. Subsequent variants have been fitted with a double baffle muzzle-brake and bore evacuator in

PROPULSION AND STEERING

The PT-76 is propelled in the water by twin water jets which are also used to steer it. By closing off one jet or the other and expelling water through nozzles in the hull side, the driver can manoeuvre the vehicle in the water.

forward

left

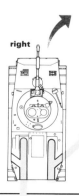

right

reverse

Gunner
The gunner acts as his own loader and, although very high rates of fire have been quoted, firing more than half a dozen shells a minute would be difficult. The gunner also has to elevate the gun manually.

Schnorkel
This fits over a ventilator in the turret rear when swimming, but can suck exhaust gases into the crew compartment.

Commander
Eyes glued to his periscopes, the commander navigates his tank ashore. Although it can cope with steep gradients ashore, the PT-76, like most amphibians, needs a gently sloping beach or bank to exit the water quickly.

Extra fuel tank
Flat fuel tanks, similar to those on the T-54/55 series tanks, can be mounted on the hull rear. Up to two can be carried on either side.

Trim vane

an attempt to soften the recoil and reduce the fumes in the turret. The PT-76B, built from the late 1950s until production ceased in 1967, is armed with the much-improved, fully stabilized D-56TM gun. It is this variant most usually found in service within the Warsaw Pact.

Turret armament

A 7.62-mm SGMT co-axial machine gun is fitted to the right of the main armament. The full complement of 40 rounds of 76.2-mm and 1,000 rounds of 7.62-mm ammunition are stowed uncomfortably beneath the turret.

The maximum range of the 76.2-mm main armament is claimed to be just over 12 km (about 7.5 miles).

But this would require full elevation and is well beyond the scope even of the TSh-66 sight fitted to the latest models. A variety of armour piercing fixed rounds can be fired. These are effective against the thin skins of APCS and armoured cars but are all hopelessly outranged by NATO anti-tank weapons. Armour piercing high explosive (APHE) and high velocity armour piercing (HVAP) rounds, weighing 6.5 kg and 3.1 kg respectively, are both capable of penetrating 60mm of armour at 1,000 metres. The High Explosive Anti Tank (HEAT) projectile, weighing 4 kg, can overcome 325mm of armour at 1,200 metres.

The only true derivatives of the

Water ducts

The water ducts suck up water from underneath the hull and expel it through the hull rear or the side nozzle. This system is more efficient than using the movement of the tracks to power a vehicle in the water.

The North Vietnamese Army used PT-76s to overrun a US Special Forces camp at Lang Vei in 1968, but they enjoyed few other successes. This one was captured by the ARVN in Laos in 1971.

PT-76 have been manufactured by the Chinese. The Type 60 light tank, first manufactured in 1966, was soon followed by the larger Type 63 still in production today. The Type 63, which has seen service in the Vietnam War, the Indo-Pakistan War of 1971 and in the Chinese invasion of Vietnam in 1979, is essentially a PT-76 chassis and powerpack mounting a larger turret and 85-mm gun.

Despite its age and its primitive engine and suspension, the basic chassis is incorporated into a number of weapon systems including, at divisional level, the SA-6 'Gainful' surface-to-air missile and GSP bridger; at regimental level, the ZSU-23-4 anti-

aircraft gun and 2S1 self-propelled howitzer, the BTR-50 APC, and several of the older FROG nuclear-capable missiles.

The future

The PT-76 is bound to remain a firm favourite of many Third World countries, if only because it is cheap and easy to maintain. But its size, lack of speed, low range and light armament make it inappropriate for any modern conflict. The Soviet army has now replaced it in the reconnaissance role by a combination of BMP-1s and BRDM-2s. The Naval Infantry keep it only because of its amphibious ability.

Over 7,000 PT-76s were built, of

Battlefield Evaluation: comparing

PT-76

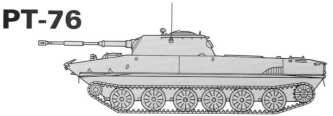

The PT-76's design was heavily influenced by Soviet experience in World War II, when the lack of amphibious light armour was an irritating problem. To achieve a reasonable amphibious performance, the PT-76 became a large and poorly protected vehicle. The lack of an NBC system in a recce vehicle is just as serious a drawback in a vehicle with one strength and many weaknesses. The only time the PT-76 really came into its own was in 1971, when the Indian Army used them in waterlogged Bangladesh.

Specification:
Crew: 3
Combat weight: 14 tonnes
Road speed: 44 km/h
Power to weight ratio: 17 hp/tonne
Length: 6.91 m
Height: 2.26 m
Armament: 1×76.2-mm gun, 1×7.62-mm machine-gun

Assessment
Firepower	★★★
Protection	★★
Age	★★★★★
Worldwide users	★★★★★

A clear view of the water jets and their hatches which propel and steer the PT-76 in the water.

AMX-13

Production of the PT-76 ended 20 years ago, but the similar AMX-13 is still available. The French vehicle is not amphibious and, similarly, lacks NBC protection, but it does at least have enough armour thickness to stop a heavy machine-gun. Armed with 75-, 90- or 105-mm guns it can destroy Main Battle Tanks not fitted with advanced armour. Half as fast again as a PT-76, it is a much more valuable reconnaissance vehicle unless fighting in the Pripet marshes or similar low-lying areas.

Specification:
Crew: 3
Combat weight: 15 tonnes
Road speed: 60 km/h
Power to weight ratio: 16.6 hp/tonne
Length: 4.9 m
Height: 2.3 m
Armament: 1×105-mm gun, 1×7.62-mm machine-gun

Assessment
Firepower	★★★★★
Protection	★★★
Age	★★★★★
Worldwide users	★★★★

Unlike the PT-76, the French AMX-13 has a reasonable chance of knocking out a Main Battle Tank.

Type 63

This is the Chinese version of the PT-76, which is heavier but faster owing to its bigger engine. It served alongside the PT-76 in the North Vietnamese Army during the Vietnam war and fought against it in 1971, when the Pakistani Army fielded limited numbers of Type 63s against Indian PT-76s. Its armour is fractionally thicker in places: 10 mm against 7 mm on the hull rear, but the vehicle is still poorly protected.

Specification:
Crew: 4
Combat weight: 18.7 tonnes
Road speed: 64 km/h
Power to weight ratio: 21.39-tonne
Length: 7.15 m
Height: 2.52 m
Armament: 1×85-mm gun, 1×7.62-mm co-axial machine-gun, 1×12.7-mm AA gun.

Assessment
Firepower	★★★
Protection	★★
Age	★★★★★
Worldwide users	★★

The Chinese Type 63 is no more than a development of the PT-76 with a more powerful main armament.

which approximately 2,000 were exported. The Soviet Union retains some 1,200 vehicles in reserve. Poland and Hungary each retain 100 operationally. The Soviets have always shown a marked reluctance to scrap any useable equipment so it is likely that they will continue to feed the surplus stock to friends and allies for many years to come.

Soviet scoff disappearing fast on exercise. Note the distinctive helmets worn by Warsaw Pact armour crew and the way the turret hatches have been locked in the vertical position, revealing the three periscopes above the commander's position on the right.

the PT-76 with its rivals

AMX-10RC

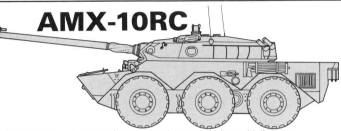

A wheeled vehicle can perform reconnaissance missions with little less capability than a tracked light tank. The AMX-10RC is a better amphibian than the PT-76 and it has an NBC system. Its 105-mm gun can destroy a Main Battle Tank and its armour protection is no worse. Large armoured cars with tank calibre armament continue to be popular with the French army, which has several vehicles of this type in service.

Specification:
Crew: 4
Combat weight: 15.8 tonnes
Road speed: 85 km/h
Power to weight ratio: 16.45 hp/tonne
Length: 6.3 m
Height: 2.7 m
Armament: 1×105-mm gun, 1×7.62-mm machine-gun

Assessment
Firepower	★★★★★
Protection	★★
Age	★★
Worldwide users	★★

Amphibious and with an NBC system, the AMX-10RC is the modern equivalent of the PT-76.

Spähpanzer Luchs

Able to travel backwards as quickly as it can drive forward, the Luchs is a well designed recce vehicle. Despite being substantially heavier, the Luchs is much faster than the underpowered Soviet PT-76 and it carries a respectable level of armour protection. It is fully amphibious and has two steerable propellers in the hull.

Specification:
Crew: 4
Combat weight: 19.5 tonnes
Road speed: 90 km/h
Power to weight ratio: 20 hp/tonne
Length: 7.74 m
Height: 2.1 m
Armament: 1×20-mm cannon, 1×7.62-mm machine-gun

Assessment
Firepower	★★
Protection	★★★
Age	★★
Worldwide users	★

The Spähpanzer Luchs is amphibious, has excellent cross-country mobility and a cannon able to chew up a PT-76.

Scorpion

The Scorpion's tiny size offers the enemy the smallest of targets, and its high speed and low ground-pressure give it an unrivalled cross country performance. Compared with the PT-76, its only weakness is lack of amphibious capability. A Scorpion can swim but needs a flotation screen raised around it, which takes several minutes to put up, while a PT-76 can splash into the water immediately. However, Scorpion is a lot more use when it gets back on dry land.

Specification:
Crew: 3
Combat weight: 8 tonnes
Road speed: 80 km/h
Power to weight ratio: 23.5 hp/tonne
Length: 4.7 m
Height: 2.1 m
Armament: 1×76.2-mm gun, 1×7.62-mm machine-gun

Assessment
Firepower	★★★★
Protection	★★★
Age	★★★
Worldwide users	★★★★

The Scorpion is not amphibious without preparation, but is superior in all other aspects to the PT-76.

Airborne Shield: the Apache Gunship

The exact number of Warsaw Pact tanks lined up against NATO remains unknown outside of privileged circles in the West, yet it is obvious to any observers that the number is enormous compared with our own forces. To combat such numerical superiority, one needs weapons that are survivable in the face of the opposition.

High tech, high expense

Many of the West's weapons are developed along such a concept, taking advantage of the technology gap between East and West to provide superweapons that are far in advance of what they are ranged against. Nowhere is that high-tech, high-expense policy more obvious than in the McDonnell Douglas AH-64 Apache attack helicopter.

Of course the US Army already has the Bell AH-1 Cobra in operation, but this lacks the all-important night and bad weather capability demanded by today's battlefield. Determined to operate the last word in sophisticated helicopters, the US Army sought a successor to the Cobra. Bell and Hughes (McDonnell Douglas after 1984) submitted designs, the latter winning with its YAH-64 design.

Below: The AH-64 is packed with sophisticated gadgets for weapons aiming. Here are night vision goggles and voice activation systems under test.

Not only is the Apache fast and strong, it is also agile: a necessary attribute over today's battlefield. Here it demonstrates that agility during flight tests.

Eight years of development led to the first production AH-64, which had changed considerably during its gestation to incorporate the latest technology. The weapon system is the most sophisticated flying today on a helicopter, capable not only of launching anti-armour missiles in any weather conditions but also of 'spotting' targets for other systems.

Target location

Central to this ability is the TADS/PNVS system. TADS (target acquisition and designation sight) incorporates a forward-looking infra-red, direct-view optics and television, all mounted in a steerable turret in the

By far the most important weapon of the AH-64 is the Rockwell Hellfire anti-tank missile. This homes on reflected laser energy, and once launched operates autonomously, allowing the Apache to return to cover. Designation usually comes from the ground, but can be provided by the AH-64 itself.

Inside the AH-64

The most sophisticated attack helicopter in the world, the McDonnell Douglas AH-64A Apache is a carefully integrated weapon system combining superb offensive capability and high survivability in the face of present and projected Soviet defences. It is set to become the West's most important anti-armour asset.

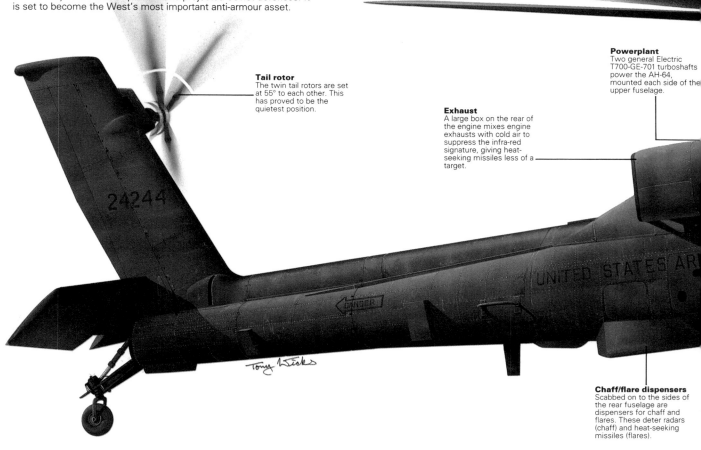

Powerplant
Two general Electric T700-GE-701 turboshafts power the AH-64, mounted each side of the upper fuselage.

Tail rotor
The twin tail rotors are set at 55° to each other. This has proved to be the quietest position.

Exhaust
A large box on the rear of the engine mixes engine exhausts with cold air to suppress the infra-red signature, giving heat-seeking missiles less of a target.

Chaff/flare dispensers
Scabbed on to the sides of the rear fuselage are dispensers for chaff and flares. These deter radars (chaff) and heat-seeking missiles (flares).

nose. These allow the co-pilot/gunner to locate the target in all weathers, after which a laser is used to designate the target for the Apache's missiles or for another weapon system.

Above the TADS is the PNVS (pilot night vision system), a fixed FLIR which allows safe flying at low level at night. Both crew members wear an IHADSS (integrated helmet and display sighting system) which allows them to aim the sensors and weapons merely by turning their heads in the direction they want. Other cockpit displays give comprehensive data on other factors such as helicopter speed, air temperature, etc. The functions of all the sensors are available in both cockpits, allowing the gunner to control the helicopter if the pilot is hit.

One criticism has been constantly levelled at the AH-64: that to use its

The Apache is entering service in large numbers with Stateside units, and has recently begun deploying to West Germany. It is here that the majority will be based in the future, able to be reinforced quickly by US-based aircraft.

nose-mounted turret means it has to expose itself to enemy fire by rising above the masking terrain. In normal operations this is not so great a problem as the AH-64 operates a considerable way back from the FEBA, and is consequently less vulnerable than other types. However, an update programme may incorporate a mast-mounted sight so that the helo can stay below tree level during attacks.

Three main weapons

Having located, designated and locked-up on targets, the AH-64 has three main weapons it can bring to bear. By far the most important is the Rockwell Hellfire anti-tank missile. This is laser-guided, and provided the target is constantly 'sparkled' by a laser designator throughout its flight will guide itself to the target. It is most effective when the designation is carried out by a ground designator or one in a light scout helicopter. This allows the Apache to break off from the attack as soon as the Hellfire is launched and engage another target.

Up to 16 Hellfires can be carried, but

Rotor head
The rotor head is topped by air data probes, which give an accurate dynamic pressure reading in the undisturbed air above the rotors.

Cockpit
The co-pilot/gunner occupies the front cockpit, with the handling pilot in the rear. An acrylic blast screen separates the two.

PNVS
The night vision system is mounted above the TADS and consists of a stabilised FLIR for safe low-level flight at night.

...mmer
...ALQ-144 turret emits ...s of infra-red energy ...nfuse heat-seeking ...es.

TADS
Carried in a trainable turret, the TADS consists of day television, direct-view optics, laser designator/tracker and forward-looking infra-red.

Chain gun
Under the nose in a collapsible mounting is housed the M230A1 Chain Gun. Capable of 625 rounds per minute, it is of 30-mm calibre.

Hellfire missiles
Four of the Rockwell Hellfire laser-guided weapons can be carried on each pylon. These track laser energy reflected from the target.

...ket pods
...e are the standard ...und 2.75-in rocket ...chers, often carried on ...utboard pylons.

a more normal load is eight, the outer wing pylons being filled by a 19-round 2.75-in rocket pod. Azimuth aiming is controlled by turning the helicopter, but elevation for the rocket firing (and consequently range) can be altered by pivoting the stub wing.

Under the nose is the 30-mm M230A1 Chain Gun, slaved to the sighting system with powered elevation and traverse, and spewing out 625 rounds per minute with deadly accuracy at maximum rate. 1,200 rounds are carried in a large box in the lower fuselage. Other ordnance can be carried, and the Apache will soon carry air-to-air missiles on the end of the stub wings, either two Sidewinders or four Stingers. Primarily for self-defence, these can also be used offensively thanks to the Apache's excellent performance and agility.

The weapon system has had a considerable effect on the look of the aircraft, but the main design criterion was survivability. Most systems are doubled up to continue working if one is hit, and the airframe incorporates many crashworthy features. The gun and undercarriage are designed to fold and soak up energy in the event of a crash, leaving the cockpit hopefully unscathed.

Kevlar and ESR (electro-slag remelt) steel are used to protect vital areas such as the crew seats and transmission. No fewer than five spars are incorporated into each of the four rotor blades, enabling them to function even after a hit from a 23-mm cannon shell.

Staying at the rear

Of course it's a lot better to avoid being hit in the first place, and the Apache has many features to keep it out of trouble. Firstly, the tactics of the AH-64 envisage it staying to the rear of the battle area, allowing other agencies to designate targets, the Apache providing the launch vehicle for the missiles. To counter enemy radars, the aircraft is equipped with chaff dispensers, and a passive radar warning receiver gives the crew warning when they are being 'painted' by hostile radars, allowing them to get to cover before attack.

Of more concern to the crews are infra-red guided missiles, fired from the shoulders of infantry in the field. To combat these the Apache has a suppressed exhaust, where the heat emitted from the engines is spread over a wider area to present less of a target to a heat-seeker. In addition an infra-red countermeasures turret emits pulses of infra-red energy which confuses missiles and forces them to break lock.

Ground crew load a Hellfire missile under the stub wing of the Apache. Up to 16 of these anti-armour missiles can be carried, although eight is the usual load, allied to unguided rocket pods.

An AH-64 presents a stark silhouette against a snowy backdrop. In its operational environment its olive drab paint and use of terrain-masking will render it a good deal less visible.

The first Apache was delivered to the US Army in January 1984, and initial operational capability was achieved in 1986. AH-64s have been delivered to Army National Guard units in addition to regulars, and a total of 675 has been ordered. Production is well over the halfway mark, and at present most of the Apaches are based in the United States.

From here it can self-deploy to many areas of the world, the aircraft demonstrating a range of 1,175 miles when fitted with ferry tanks, adequate to take them to Europe via the northern Atlantic route. If it is required more urgently in the battlezone, or the sectors are beyond its range capabil-

ities, it can be deployed by Lockheed C-141 or C-5 transports with a minimum of disassembly.

West German deployment

However, it is the German battlefield for which the AH-64 has been designed, and the near future will see the establishment of several companies in West Germany, to fight alongside the Bell AH-1 Cobra on anti-armour missions. It will operate in close concert with Fairchild A-10s in the Joint Air Attack Team concept, whereby the helicopter and fixed-wing aircraft engage the enemy together, with the helicopter attacking while the A-10 repositions for its

Battlefield Evaluation: comparing

McDonnell Douglas AH-64 Apache

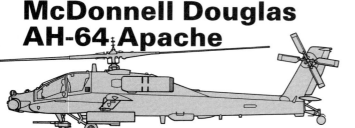

Currently the world's most sophisticated battlefield helicopter, the AH-64 possesses full adverse conditions fighting capability, with laser designation, FLIR and Hellfire missiles. The main drawbacks to the type are the lack of mast- or roof-mounted sight, and the large unit cost.

Specification:
Length overall: 17.76m
Rotor diameter: 14.63m
Maximum cruising speed: 155 knots
Range: 482km
Standard weapon load: M230 30-mm Chain Gun; 16 Hellfire anti-tank missiles

Assessment
Manoeuvrability ★★★
All weather capability ★★★★★
Versatility ★★
Worldwide users ★

The AH-64 is the most feared gunship helo in the world, heavily armed and with sophisticated weaponry.

Bell AH-1F HueyCobra

The AH-64's partner in the helicopter attack team is the AH-1F Cobra, the latest version of the original gunship helicopter. Although available in large numbers, the Cobra suffers from lack of bad weather capability and cannot fire the Hellfire missile. Modification programmes in the future may rectify this.

Specification:
Length overall: 16.18m
Rotor diameter: 13.41m
Maximum cruising speed: 123 knots
Range: 507km
Standard weapon load: eight TOW anti-tank missiles; one three-barrelled 20-mm cannon; two unguided rocket or cannon pods

Assessment
Manoeuvrability ★★★
All weather capability ★
Versatility ★
Worldwide users ★★★★

Smaller cousin of the AH-64, the AH-1F is the current upgraded model of the trusty Cobra.

Bell AH-1T and AH-1W

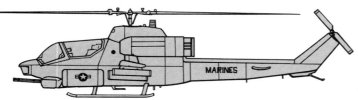

Differing primarily from the Army Cobras by having twin engines for overwater safety, the Marine Corps aircraft carry different ordnance loads, including the Hellfire missile in the case of the AH-1W. Like the Apache, the Marine Corps aircraft are also fitted for air-to-air fighting, carrying Sidewinder missiles.

Specification:
Length overall: 17.68m
Rotor diameter: 14.63m
Maximum cruising speed: 189 knots
Range: 635km
Standard weapon load: eight TOW or Hellfire anti-tank missiles; one three-barrel 20-mm cannon; up to 76 2.75-in unguided rockets or 16 5-in Zuni rockets or cannon pods or two AIM-9L Sidewinder air-to-air missiles

Assessment
Manoeuvrability ★★★
All weather capability ★★★
Versatility ★★★
Worldwide users ★★

The twin-engined Marine Corps Cobra has Hellfire and Sidewinder capability.

attack and vice versa. In such a way the defences have no respite.

Commanders, aircrew and ground crew alike are enthusiastic about the Apache. An aircraft designed specifically for the job of tank-killing has been a long time coming to the US Army, and it has been welcomed into service. Certainly its capabilities are way in advance of anything flying anywhere else in the world. Whether the proposed Marine Corps and Navy versions go ahead remains to be seen, but in the meantime the Apache has tipped the numerical balance back to NATO, and given its commanders the tool with which to take on the Soviet tank masses.

Traversing at medium altitude, the AH-64 has a good range, particularly if ferry tanks are carried in place of the armament. It can deploy to Europe from America by itself, a remarkable feat for an attack helicopter.

the AH-64 with its rivals

Agusta A 129 Mangusta

A dedicated anti-tank helicopter from Italy, the Mangusta is roughly comparable to the AH-1F in terms of capability. TOW missiles are the primary weapon, and it possesses good agility. As with the AH-64 it at present has no mast-mounted sight, a definite drawback in the battlefield.

Specification:
Length overall: 14.29 m
Rotor diameter: 11.90 m
Maximum cruising speed: 140 knots
Range: not quoted
Standard weapon load: eight TOW missiles; two rocket or 20-mm cannon pods

Assessment
Manoeuvrability ★★★
All weather capability ★★★★
Versatility ★★
Worldwide users ★

Similar in appearance to the AH-64, the A 129 is much cheaper and less sophisticated.

Westland Lynx AH.Mk 1

Although possessing a cabin for eight troops, the Lynx is nevertheless a superb anti-armour helicopter, being amongst the most manoeuvrable of contemporary aircraft. In addition to anti-tank missions of its own, it is often used to position MILAN anti-tank teams near the front line.

Specification:
Length overall: 15.163 m
Rotor diameter: 12.80 m
Maximum cruising speed: 140 knots
Range: 540 km
Standard weapon load: eight TOW missiles

Assessment
Manoeuvrability ★★★★★
All weather capability ★
Versatility ★★★★★
Worldwide users ★

Agility, speed and TOW missiles make the Lynx an excellent anti-armour platform

Mil Mi-24 'Hind-E'

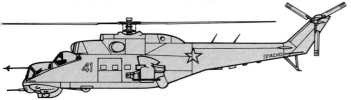

Fast and well-armoured, the various marks of Mi-24 are available in large numbers, and carry heavy weapons loads. Although excellent in the assault role using their weaponry to suppress defences while landing small teams of specialist troops, they are rather bulky and cumbersome for the dedicated anti-armour role.

Specification:
Length overall: 21.50 m
Rotor diameter: 17.00 m
Maximum cruising speed: 159 knots
Range: 750 km
Standard weapon load: four UV-32-57 rocket pods; four AT-6 'Spiral' anti-tank missiles; one four-barrel 12.7-mm cannon

Assessment
Manoeuvrability ★
All weather capability ★
Versatility ★★★
Worldwide users ★★★★★

Considerably larger than Western gunships, the 'Hind' is a capable machine.

Watch Your Step!

Mine awareness

Typical Landmine

Fuze

Body

Main Charge

Booster

Detonator

Explosive Train

1
Firing Pin Sets
Off Small Primer

2
Primer Produces
Flame or Concussion

3
Flame or Primer
Detonation -
Sets Off Detonator

4
Detonator Produces
Small Detonation

5
Detonater
Detonation
Sets Off
Booster

6
Booster Produces
Larger Detonation

7
Booster
Detonation
Sets Off
Main Charge

8
Main Charge
Produces Explosion

In order to give yourself a reasonable chance of survival, you must know what you are looking for and, equally important, how it works. Anti-tank mines generally follow the layout shown above and are detonated by an initiating action (perhaps you stepping on it) which fires a series of explosions known as the explosive train. If the train is broken at any point, the mine may not detonate. Beware: a mine may have more than one explosive train.

A large Viet Cong land mine found on a beach near a US base is detonated by engineers. Most of the VC's mines and explosive matériel came not from North Vietnam but from ordnance and mines retrieved from South Vietnamese and American units. Booby traps and mines caused 11 per cent of the deaths and 15 per cent of wounds in Vietnam, in comparison to Korea or World War II where the percentage of wounds and deaths caused by mines and booby traps was around four per cent.

A selection of dangerous ordnance to be found on the Falklands battlefields in addition to mines gives some idea of the scope of the problem. Most can be used as improvised explosive devices in a war zone.

The war is over and the soldiers departed. The odd rusting tank or water-filled crater bears mute witness to years of bitter fighting, but civilian traffic now passes over rebuilt roads and bridges. As you pass across a field towards the edge of the village there is a dull boom from across the track. The plough stops dead, the ox stands patiently. But the farmer lies in a bloody heap. The troops may have returned to barracks, but their mines remain on duty.

Combat zones and old battlefields the world over are dominated by minefields. Vietnam, Laos and Cambodia remain littered with mines; the old infiltration routes along the borders were showered with air-dropped mines by the US Air Force, and unexploded ordnance in the south continues to inflict casualties. Afghanistan has been similarly

treated by the Soviet forces, leading to the joke about how, before the war, good Muslim women walked meekly behind their husbands: now they have to walk in front.

Throughout North Africa the desert still conceals lethal left-overs from World War II, and in the western Sahara the Polisario guerrillas and the Moroccan army are both sowing new fields. In the Falklands, tiny plastic anti-personnel mines are moved out of the marked danger areas by the winter storms and continue to present a serious hazard. You may be lucky and never need to know how to survive the mined battlefield; but if, by accident or design, you find yourself tip-toeing across eggshells in some foreign field, a knowledge of mines could mean the difference between life and death.

A bewildering selection of mines confronts any soldier trying to learn how to counter them. Different nations manufacture mines, producing similar effects but of totally different construction. The only general preparation you can make is to learn how mines are used, how they are constructed and how armies mark minefields and make them safe for themselves.

But if you're on operations against an unexpected opponent, you won't have a chance to become familiar with his mines prior to hostilities. This is what happened to the sappers of the Falklands Task Force, who had little idea of the types of mines used by the Argentines. In the end, young sappers had to infiltrate booby-trapped minefields and recover examples of live mines.

Mines are being developed with increasing sophistication to keep phase with their primary target – the battle tank – and have an enormous psych-

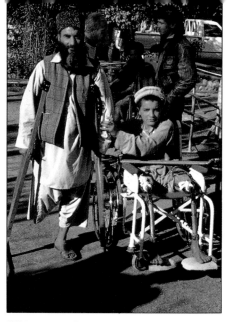

Widespread Soviet mining of Afghanistan with air-droppable mines such as the PFM-1, known to the Afghans as the Green Parrot, has inflicted severe casualties. These are the lucky ones.

ological as well as physical impact on an enemy. If you are to survive the mined battlefield, you must appreciate that you are in as much danger from 'friendly' devices as you are from your enemy's. Remember, the mine is a double-edged weapon.

The basic principles

A mine is made up of a fuse, a detonator, a booster (sometimes), a main charge, and a body or case. An initiating action causes the fuse to function and this starts the explosive train, whereby a flame or concussion is caused by electrical or mechanical means and is applied to the detonator. This then sets off the booster, if there is one, or the main charge. A variety of initiating actions can set off the process:

1 Pressure (downward force caused by a man's foot or the wheel or track of a vehicle).

Above: The component parts of this Italian mine used in the Falklands clearly show the explosive train. The top plastic cover contains the fuse assembly and detonator. The two cheese shapes in the middle are the main charge and the booster charge.

Right: An unmarked Argentine minefield shows two rows of SB 81 Italian plastic anti-tank mines. These are relatively easy to find and lift.

Safing

The Argentines used vast quantities of Italian-made SB 33 anti-personnel mines. It is a plastic irregular shape with a large pressure pad, and should therefore be handled by the sides. To safe the mine, insert the safety pin in the side.

Then unscrew the detonator from the base of the mine using a coin. All mines have roughly similar methods of safing, but you must learn the safing methods for all the mines you are likely to encounter.

2 Pulling (on a tripwire attached to the fuse).

3 Tension release (release of tension, such as cutting a tripwire, that prevents the fuse from acting).

4 Pressure release (release of pressure that prevents the fuse from acting).

5 Electrical (closing a circuit that activates the fuse).

6 Timer rundown (a preset timer arrives at a point that activates the fuse).

Other types of initiating actions include vibrations, magnetic influence, frequency induction and audiofrequency.

Types of mine

There are three main types of mine: anti-tank, anti-personnel, and chemical. Anti-tank mines, designed to damage or destroy tanks and other vehicles and their occupants, can be blast-type, disabling wheels or tracks; vertical penetration, attacking the bottom of a vehicle; or horizontal effect, placed off routes to attack the side of vehicles.

Anti-personnel mines are designed

Methods of initiating mines

Mines and booby traps d[...] explode only when you s[...] them: any one, or severa[...] these methods could be [...] to fire a single device. Yo[...] must be aware of all of th[...] as they are the ways you [...] be injured or killed on the[...] battlefield.

Pressure from the downward force of a man's boot or a tank track.

Pressure release by removal of a weight that keeps the fuse from acting.

Tension release, for example by cutting a trip wire that prevents the fuse from acting.

Pulling on a trip wire that is attached to the fuse.

Magnetic influence, from large metal objects such as tanks, which fires the fuse.

Frequence induction: radi[...] controlled detonation by an observer.

Command detonation: electrical firing by an observer.

Audio frequency: sensitivity to the sound of particular engine noise.

Timer run-down, set to explode after a fixed period of time.

Vibration: the fuse is set to a geophone which senses the vibrations in the ground from armoured vehicles.

to disable or kill personnel. The blast type have an explosive charge and detonate when stepped on. Fragmentation types contain shrapnel or have a case which fragments when the main charge fires, and are divided into static mines (which detonate in place), bounding mines (which bound into the air and explode several feet above the ground), and horizontal effect mines (which expel a spray of shrapnel in one direction).

Not all mines are harmful. You may come across phoney mines – dummies planted to make the enemy think they have found a live one, and waste time tackling it or avoiding it.

Handling mines

Like any other explosive material, mines and their fuses must be handled carefully. Most mines have safety devices to stop them going off by accident or prematurely, but as a soldier you may also find yourself having to improvise mines in the field, so get used to taking great care.

Any amount of explosive can be fused and placed as a mine. Grenades and some demolition charges already have fuse wells for installing firing devices; bombs, mortars and artillery shells can be used; and incendiary fuels in containers can be rigged as flame mines. The aspects of handling mines are:

1 Fusing
This means installing the detonator and fuse assembly. Fuse wells should be clean and free of foreign matter when the fuse and detonator are put in.

2 Arming
When the fuse is installed, you arm

Handling mines

You've got to know what you're doing with mines, before you have to deal with them: learning by experience can be a little traumatic. This is a Russian TMN 46 anti-tank, anti-lift mine. The important point about this mine is that there is a second detonator well in the base of the mine, so it can be easily booby-trapped. The mine is very similar to the TM 46, which does not have the anti-handling device.

the mine by removing all safety devices. The mine is then ready to function.

3 Safing
In general, this is the reverse of arming. If you put the mine in place yourself and kept it in sight the whole time, you can remove it from its hold for safing. If not, attach a long rope or wire, take cover, and pull the mine from the hole. Safing involves checking the sides and bottom of the mine for anti-handling devices and disarming them if found; replacing all pins, clips or other safety devices; turning the arm-

ing dial, if there is one, to 'Safe' or 'Unarmed'; and removing the fuse and, if possible, the detonator.

4 Neutralising
This means destroying the mine if safing is thought to be too risky, as in the case of improvised mines which will probably be unstable and dangerous. But do not detonate chemical mines: they will contaminate the area.

Anti-handling techniques

There are several devices for preventing someone disabling a mine. Enterprising engineers are apt to booby-trap their mines to make it difficult and dangerous to clear them. Anti-lift or anti-handling devices, when attached to a mine, will detonate the mine or another charge nearby if the mine is lifted or pulled out of its hole. An anti-disturbance device sets off the explosion if the mine is disturbed or shaken. Shielded, twisted firing wire can be attached to command-detonated mines to defeat enemy ECM. Long pulse or multi-pulse fuses can defeat tank mine-clearing rollers and explosive mine-clearing charges.

Another way of dealing with mine-clearing rollers is to place an unfused anti-tank mine (or explosive charge) in the ground, connected with detonating cord to a pressure fuse or firing device about three metres away. The roller then rolls over the unfused mine and activates the fuse when the tank itself is over the mine or charge.

Anti-handling devices

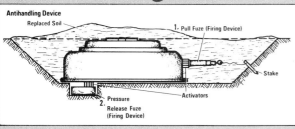

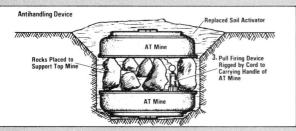

Most anti-tank mines cannot be set off by a man's weight, so unless they are used in conjunction with AP mines, infantry could lift them. For this reason, many mines will have anti-handling devices fitted to additional detonator wells.

Slightly more sneaky is the use of a second mine to booby-trap the first using a pull-firing device. Most anti-tank mines are equipped with extra detonator wells, but the same effect can be achieved with quantities of explosive placed with the mine.

Survival

Detecting Mines

Mines vary in scale from anti-personnel weapons such as the US 'gravel' mine, shaped like and little bigger than a tea-bag, to massive anti-tank mines designed to pierce armour plate and destroy a 60-tonne armoured vehicle. The sheer diversity of modern mines rules out any single answer to them. All you can do is to employ as many techniques and procedures as possible. Each one provides a degree of safety; combined, they can significantly weaken a powerful weapon.

Military counter-mine operations consist of detection of individual mines; breaching and clearing minefields; reconnaissance for minefields; sowing a cleared enemy minefield with your own mines; prevention of enemy mining; and detection of enemy minelaying. In combat you must make full use of all intelligence-gathering resources to obtain enemy mine information. This will enable you to plan the use of sensors, aggressive countermining or other tactics as necessary to defeat his efforts. There are six basic rules to surviving the mined battlefield:

Denial of opportunity

Aggressive patrolling prevents the enemy laying his mines. The effects of patrols can be increased with night vision aids and sentry or scout dogs. In addition, sensors can be used on major routes and areas where enemy mining is heavy; sensors can alert

The Argentine forces extensively mined the Falkland Islands and failed to keep proper records. British forces cleared many areas but some sectors remain closed off, sanctuaries for the penguins who are too light to set off a mine.

quick reaction forces to move in on the threatened area, or can be used to bring fire on the enemy. However, US forces in Vietnam never really found an answer to local guerrillas mining the roads – the infantry manpower needed for intensive patrolling was seldom available. South African forces are painfully aware how easy it is to mine isolated roads near their

Dogs are widely used as explosive sniffers in internal security work. They were useful in Vietnam where the enemy rarely coverd his booby traps with fire, regarding them as an obstacle to hinder movement.

borders and have developed mine-resistant vehicles designed to survive anti-tank mines.

Detection

The best way of detecting mines is by direct vision combined with a knowledge of minelaying methods. On the principle of setting a thief to catch a thief, if you understand how to plant mines properly, you will have a much better grasp of mine detection. Sweep teams made up of trained observers, men with electronic detectors, and probers have proved highly effective, but security forces must be deployed to the flanks and rear of sweep teams to avoid ambush. Mine and tunnel dogs have been used with success to detect booby traps, tripwires, unexploded ordnance, punji pits and arms caches, as well as enemy troops. These dogs should be used with other detection systems, not as a single system.

Denial of material

The enemy may rely on captured material for his conduct of mine warfare. This is especially true in guerrilla warfare: in Vietnam, many Viet Cong booby-traps used captured American ordnance. VC sappers were also known to infiltrate American perimeters protected with Claymore mines and reverse them so that they exploded in the wrong direction. Strict measures must be taken to deny the enemy all materials which can be used for mine warfare.

Intelligence

There must be a complete system for reporting mine incidents. Analysis of reports may be combined with communication intelligence sources. The purpose is to reveal areas of heavy mining by the enemy as well as the types of mines and firing devices used.

Training

Proper training reduces casualties from mines and booby traps. Intensive unit level training should be conducted on how the enemy emplaces and camouflages these weapons.

Protective measures

These measures may include the wearing of body armour and helmets by sweep teams, sandbagging the flooring of vehicles, and requiring the occupants to keep their arms and legs inside. In the South African Army it is now a chargeable offence not to be strapped into your harness when riding in a Buffel-type APC. Soldiers on foot must avoid bunching up at the site of a mine detonation: the enemy may have placed other mines to take advantage of this natural tendency.

Detection and search

Detection of mines is an action performed by soldiers in all phases of combat; search is a more deliberate action taken by single soldiers, teams or small units to locate mines or minefields. The following techniques are recommended for both.

1 Do not wear sunglasses: with them, you are less able to detect tripwires and camouflage.
2 Be alert for tripwires in these places:
 ★ across trails
 ★ on the shoulders of roads at likely ambush sites

★ near known or suspected anti-tank or anti-vehicle mines
★ across the best route through dense plant growth
★ in villages and on roads or paths into them
★ in and around likely helicopter landing sites
★ in approaches to enemy positions
★ at bridges, fords and ditches
★ across rice paddy dikes

3 Check anything that might conceal a mine or its triggering device:
 ★ mud smears, grass, sticks, dirt, dung or other material on roads
 ★ signs of road repair, for example new covering or paving, ditch and drainage work
 ★ tyremarks, skidmarks or ruts

4 Be alert for signs that might belong to, mark or point to hidden mines:
 ★ signs on trees, posts or stakes, or signs painted on the road. Most are small and not easy to spot
 ★ marks other than signs, for instance sticks or stones placed in a line, clumps of grass placed at intervals. Look for patterns not present in nature
 ★ wires leading away from the side of a road; they may be command firing wires
 ★ odd items in trees, branches or bushes; they may be explosive grenades, mortar rounds or artillery shells
 ★ odd features in the ground, for instance wilting plant camouflage

5 Watch the civilians. They may know where local mines are, so see where they don't go — for instance, one

Mines are a prime weapon of the guerrilla enemies of the South African Army, which now leads the world in mine protected vehicles. The AC200 is the latest of their multi-purpose wheeled AFVs and is designed to offer the optimum protection against mines.

The 40-mm grenades fired by the American M79 grenade-launcher were widely used by the Viet Cong, who picked them up from landing zones or old US positions. Hand grenades tucked into webbing by the pin often fell out too.

side of the road, or certain buildings.
6 Be careful of any equipment left behind by, or belonging to, the enemy: it may be booby-trapped.
7 Listen for the sound of a delayed fuse device. If you think you hear one, get down — fast.
8 Do not use any metal object as a probe: the metal can close the circuit between contacts. Use sharpened wooden sticks. When feeling for tripwires, use a lightweight stick.
9 Use scout dog teams to detect booby traps.
10 Check all entrances (to buildings, caves, tunnels etc) for booby traps, and search the approaches and surrounding area for anti-personnel mines.
11 If you find an anti-tank mine, inspect by eye and probe for anti-handling devices.

Positions for mines

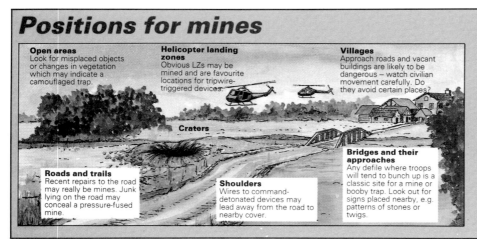

Open areas
Look for misplaced objects or changes in vegetation which may indicate a camouflaged trap.

Helicopter landing zones
Obvious LZs may be mined and are favourite locations for tripwire-triggered devices.

Villages
Approach roads and vacant buildings are likely to be dangerous – watch civilian movement carefully. Do they avoid certain places?

Craters

Roads and trails
Recent repairs to the road may really be mines. Junk lying on the road may conceal a pressure-fused mine.

Shoulders
Wires to command-detonated devices may lead away from the road to nearby cover.

Bridges and their approaches
Any defile where troops will tend to bunch up is a classic site for a mine or booby trap. Look out for signs placed nearby, e.g. patterns of stones or twigs.

Recognising signs of mine laying

Finding a mine before it finds you depends on concentration and experience. American units in Vietnam found that they suffered fewer losses to mines in the morning, at the beginning of a patrol when everyone was fresh, but more in the afternoon when the troops were tired. Bearing this in mind, it is a good idea to change the point element regularly so that the strain of leading the column is shared evenly.

12 Remember that the enemy can use command-detonated mines. Search and clear road shoulders and surrounding areas before other mine-clearing work. Make sure you cover all potential firing positions and remove any wires and booby traps. Buried firing wires can be exposed and cut by single-toothed rooters running along 10 to 50 metres from the road. Protect the clearing party with security forces.

Probing

Probing is a way of detecting mines by piercing the earth with a sharp but non-metallic object, e.g. a pointed

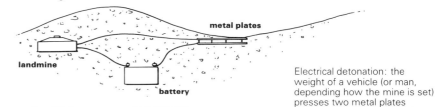

Old ruts in the road are dangerous: stay out of them. Here the pressure of a vehicle's tyres pulls the wire connected to the pins of the grenades. The grenades explode, setting off the main charges. Note the mine on the right by the side of the road, where troops are likely to try and take cover during an ambush.

Electrical detonation: the weight of a vehicle (or man, depending how the mine is set) presses two metal plates together. This completes the electrical circuit, detonating the mine.

Guerrilla mine tactics

If mines are laid in a group, they will usually be in a logical pattern. This may be dictated by the ground, but will often follow a fixed formula. These three patterns of mine laying were widely used by guerrillas during the Rhodesian war. They use the minimum number of their precious anti-tank mines to give the best chance of hitting a vehicle.

Note the invariable habit of planting most of the mines in the ruts worn in the road. Despite all warnings, it is very easy to follow the smoother route of old tracks and become another victim. Remember that, when actually following another vehicle, the reverse is true and you are obviously safest by following the leading vehicle's exact route.

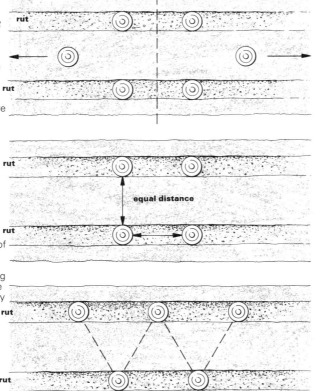

If you do not have a proper mine probe handy, use a bit of plank or a stick. A metal object such as your bayonet could connect electrical circuits, detonating an electrically-fused or magnetic influence mine. Push in gently at an angle of about 45 degrees, as shown above.

The SB-33 is an Italian anti-personnel mine encountered in the Falklands. It is just 88mm across and very hard to spot, since its green plastic skin weathers quickly. An ingenious mechanism prevents it exploding if banged sharply, but the gradual pressure of a foot sets it off.

Emergency drill

Above: Caught in a minefield under fire, you are dead unless you can escape quickly. One desperate measure is to bang your Bergen ahead of you as an improvised mine roller.

Left: In an emergency you may have to use your bayonet to prod for mines and just hope that they don't have magnetically influenced fuses or electrical detonation devices.

stick. It is slow and hard work but is probably the most reliable way to find mines. When probing, follow this procedure:

1 Move on your hands and knees or stay prone. Look and feel upward and forward for tripwires or pressure prongs. Keep your sleeves rolled up and remove watches and rings – your sense of touch must be at its keenest.

2 After looking and feeling the ground, probe every five centimetres across a one-metre frontage. Press the probe gently into the ground at an angle of less than 45 degrees from horizontal. Never push the probe straight down or you may detonate a pressure mine.

3 If the probe won't go in freely, the soil must be picked away with the tip of the probe and the loose earth or stones removed by hand.

4 If you touch a solid object, stop probing, remove the earth by hand and check it out.

5 If you find a mine, remove just enough of the surrounding soil to see what type it is. Then report it.

Caution: If you know or suspect the enemy is using magnetically influenced fuses, make sure no-one is carrying anything made of iron or steel in the vicinity of the mines. This means no steel helmets, bayonets, rifles etc.

Correct detection methods

A Royal Marine demonstrates the correct use of the mine probe. Clearing a minefield by hand is a risky business, but often a necessary preliminary to a set-piece assault.

As you probe your way slowly forward, the cleared lane must be marked for the following troops and mines you have located clearly signposted. Here the clearing party places a plastic marker near a mine which will later be neutralised by the engineers.

Avoiding Mines

Left: The rules of war state that all minefields must be marked, with the exception of 'small nuisance clusters'. You can assume that road junctions are a profitable spot to lay mines. These mines were very hurriedly surface-laid by retreating Egyptians at a road junction patrolled by the UN.

The US Army manual on mine warfare says, 'train to prevent panic'. This is easy to say but rather harder to achieve. As you stand on a jungle trail with a screaming legless man in front of you, just what do you do? Rushing out of a live minefield is an obvious recipe for disaster, but staying put in combat will probably leave you in a killing ground under heavy fire. There is no guaranteed safe way out of a minefield, but if you know what different mines look like and understand how they work and the correct way of moving to safety, then you are in with a chance.

The only certain way of surviving the mined battlefield is to avoid blundering into a minefield in the first place. Although the famous skull and crossbones sign with *'Achtung Minen'* written above will only be seen in the cinema. NATO and Warsaw Pact forces do mark their minefields. Memorise the signs illustrated here. NATO minefields are signposted on the friendly side with triangular red markers; the side nearer the enemy is only shown by a single strand of wire about knee high.

Marking safe lanes is a tedious and labour-intensive job. The US Army uses the Hunting Lightweight Marking System, a set of steel-tipped plastic poles and yellow reflective tape. The kit is man-portable and the pins are robust enough to be hammered through tarmac. Unfortunately, not all armies are so diligent: witness the way the Argentinians scattered mines all over the Falkland Islands without even keeping a proper record of their position.

Below: Avoiding mines is largely a question of common sense. In this picture the first line of Argentine trenches was in the rocks in the foreground. The Italian anti-tank mine detonating forward of the first ridge marks the start of the protective minefield for the position. The ridge protecting the EOD vehicle from the blast is an obvious approach route and an obvious place for mines, as it is the only place that provides cover from the position's direct fire weapons.

Air-dropped mines

The Soviets have mined many guerrilla infiltration routes in Afghanistan with air-dropped devices. Similar mines were used by the US Army in South-East Asia, and they will no doubt continue to be encountered in counter-insurgency campaigns throughout the world. They are quick to lay and highly effective: Italian VS50 mines can be dropped by helicopter at a rate of 2,000 per pass. They are also the one type of minefield you can escape by rapid withdrawal from the area if you are unfortunate enough to have them dropped on your current position. Most air-dropped mines do not arm themselves for a couple of minutes, but you should make sure your identification is correct before hot-footing it away. Other characteristics of air-dropped mines are:

1 Fuses can be delay, pressure or magnetic.
2 Anti-tank and anti-personnel mines may be dropped together.
3 Most will self-destruct within a few days or even hours, but do not bank on them all self-destructing at the same time. Mines that self-destruct can be useful for security forces, which can then sweep the area in safety after the mines have done their damage.

Soviet liquid mines

One type of scatterable mine introduced by the Soviets in Afghanistan deserves a mention, although full details are not yet available. They are small plastic cells filled with liquid explosives and are camouflaged or even shaped to look like transistor

The only British aerial mines are deployed from JP 233 pods along with runway-cratering charges for putting runways out of commission. The Warsaw Pact has systems specifically devoted to mining from helicopters, fixed-wing aircraft and multi-barrelled rocket launchers.

radios, dolls or other harmless items. They detonate when moved or compressed and are thought to contain an unstable explosive similar to nitroglycerine, which is safer when frozen. They are yet another good reason to be alert to the presence of booby traps. Stay switched on even when there is no obvious danger.

Mine injuries

One of the most widely encountered types of mine is the Soviet PMD series of wooden anti-personnel mines. Simple to lay and difficult to detect, they are used by guerrilla forces all over the world as well as by the Warsaw Pact. They are activated

'Redfire', a remote-control explosive ordnance disposal vehicle, moves into an Argentine minefield. Note the wire at waist and ankle height and the 'DANGER MINES' sign, which would not be seen in wartime: this is for the benefit of the civilians who may not recognise the normal military triangle.

NATO minefield marking

mine will attack anyone unfortunate enough
step on it: your own protective minefields will
e a major hazard to your own troops. You must
ow what signs are used to mark minefields,
d you must be able to read the map.

All minefields will be marked as below, with
e exception of 'nuisance clusters'. The area
Il be fenced with a strand at ankle and waist
eight with the 'Mines' inverted triangle every
0m. Minefield safe lanes will only be marked
the friendly side, and maximum use will be
ade of existing fences, so look at the signs:
t at the type of fence.

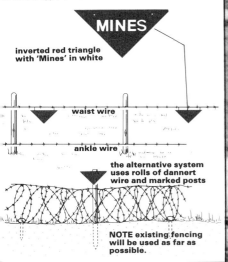

MINES

inverted red triangle with 'Mines' in white

waist wire

ankle wire

the alternative system uses rolls of dannert wire and marked posts

NOTE existing fencing will be used as far as possible.

1. The PFM-1 is dropped from fixed-wing aircraft or rockets in containers.

1. This is the famous 'Green Parrot' or PFM-1, widely seen in Afghanistan.

2. The PMD-57 is a wooden cased mine, shown here with the pressure plate open.

3. The OZM-4 is a bounding mine developed from the OZM wartime device.

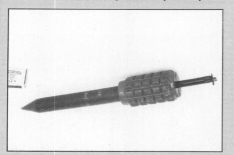

4. The POMZ-2M is a prefragmented stake mine.

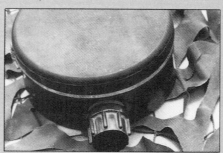

5. The PMN is a plastic mine with a rubber cover developed after WW II.

Soviet anti-personnel mines

Before you launch yourself onto the battlefield you must have a thorough knowledge of Warsaw Pact mines.

1 The PFM-1 AP mine/bomblet
Air-delivered, plastic and filled with liquid explosive, this has a bulbous, irregularly-shaped body coloured green, sand or arctic white. Any distortion of the body will fire it: this includes light pressure while handling. It does not self-destruct and cannot be neutralised.

2 The PMD series
This wooden box has a hinged lid, overlapping the sides with a deep groove cut in it above the fuse assembly, and rests on the striker retaining pin. Some have a safety rod locking the lid. Pressure on the lid forces the winged retaining nut from the striker and fires the mine.

3 OZM 4
Pressure, command or tripwire detonated, this bounds 1.5-2.4 metres into the air and explodes, showering fragments over a 50-m diameter.

4 POMZ-2M
A wooden stake with cast iron fragmentation body, activated by tripwire, this can be neutralised by securing the striker retaining pin and removing the wire. It is normally laid in clusters of three of four.

5 The PMN
The rubber-covered pressure plate on top of this small plastic mine is secured to the body by a thin metal band. The mine has a side hole for the firing mechanism and primer charge, opposite which is an initiator adaptor. The mine is armed 15-20 minutes after removing the safety pin.

The problem with modern plastic mines is that they do not always stay where you put them. This Argentine C3B plastic anti-tank mine has been washed up on a beach previously thought clear from a minefield several kilometres away.

by pressure and were encountered by members of 22 SAS serving in Oman. It was observed that the local 'Firqha' – tribesmen fighting for the government and officered by SAS personnel – suffered less damage than the SAS if they stepped on a mine: treading on a PMD generally led to the tribesman losing his toes, but SAS men in DMS or desert boots lost their whole foot at the ankle. British soldiers unfortunate enough to be wearing highneck boots like the US Cocorran jump boots often lost their leg up to the knee. Mines, like all explosives, will take the line of least resistance to cut.

Unfortunately it is not true to say that you can always minimise injury by swapping your combat boots for a pair of Ho Chi Minh sandals. In the Vietnam war, the tiny American 'gravel' anti-personnel mines contained only a very small charge. It was enough to cripple someone wearing light footwear but a hefty pair of boots would actually reduce the damage. Moral of the tale: find out what mines you may be facing, and act accordingly.

Where to expect mines

Mines are frequently positioned in specific locations rather than laid in rows in a field like potatoes. Favourite sites are roads and trails, especially junctions and bottlenecks. They may have been placed to block one route while troops observe another, ready to engage a target with direct fire. In jungle or thick forest the available tracks are screamingly obvious places to choke with mines, forcing the enemy to hack his way noisily through the undergrowth.

Warsaw Pact anti-tank mines

1 TH-62
This family of mines come in plastic, metal, wood or waterproof cardboard casings and are detonated by 175-600 kg, so a man's weight will not usually set them off. They have a two-second delay, so the tank is well over the mine when it explodes.

2 TM-46
The commonest mine in Soviet service, this has a metal body and can be laid by hand or machine. It is pressure-plate activated with an operating force of 210 kg.

3 TMN-46
Like the TM-46, this is activated by 210 kg pressure and can be fitted with a tilt rod fuse. The important difference is the extra fuse well in the bottom of the mine for booby-trapping.

4 TMD-B
This is a wooden box mine dating from World War II. The top three slats are pressure boards, the middle one is hinged to allow the fuse to be inserted. When armed the pressure board is held in place with a wooden locking bar.

5 TMA-3
A Yugoslavian plastic mine with no metallic parts found all over the world, this is blast and water resistant. It has three fuse wells and a fourth in the bottom for booby-trapping. Operating weight is 180-350 kg.

6 MRUD anti-personnel mine
The Yugoslavian equivalent of the Claymore, this fires 650 steel balls over a 60-degree arc with a lethal radius of 50 m. Activated by tripwire or remote control, it will not damage tanks but will wreck soft-skin vehicles.

1. This is the Soviet TM-62M metallic anti-tank mine.

2. The Soviet TM-46 is probably the most widely copied mine in service.

3. The TMN-46 is almost identical to the TM-46 but can be easily booby-trapped.

4. The TMD-B is a cheap, easy to produce wooden mine.

5. The TMA-3 is completely plastic and difficult to detect.

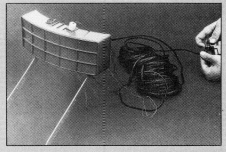

6. The MRUD is a cheap but nasty copy of the US Claymore mine.

Soviet minefield marking

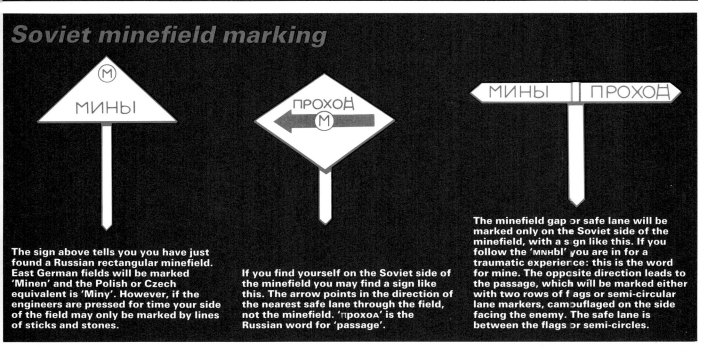

The sign above tells you you have just found a Russian rectangular minefield. East German fields will be marked 'Minen' and the Polish or Czech equivalent is 'Miny'. However, if the engineers are pressed for time your side of the field may only be marked by lines of sticks and stones.

If you find yourself on the Soviet side of the minefield you may find a sign like this. The arrow points in the direction of the nearest safe lane through the field, not the minefield. 'проход' is the Russian word for 'passage'.

The minefield gap or safe lane will be marked only on the Soviet side of the minefield, with a sign like this. If you follow the 'мины' you are in for a traumatic experience: this is the word for mine. The opposite direction leads to the passage, which will be marked either with two rows of flags or semi-circular lane markers, camouflaged on the side facing the enemy. The safe lane is between the flags or semi-circles.

Fighting Fit

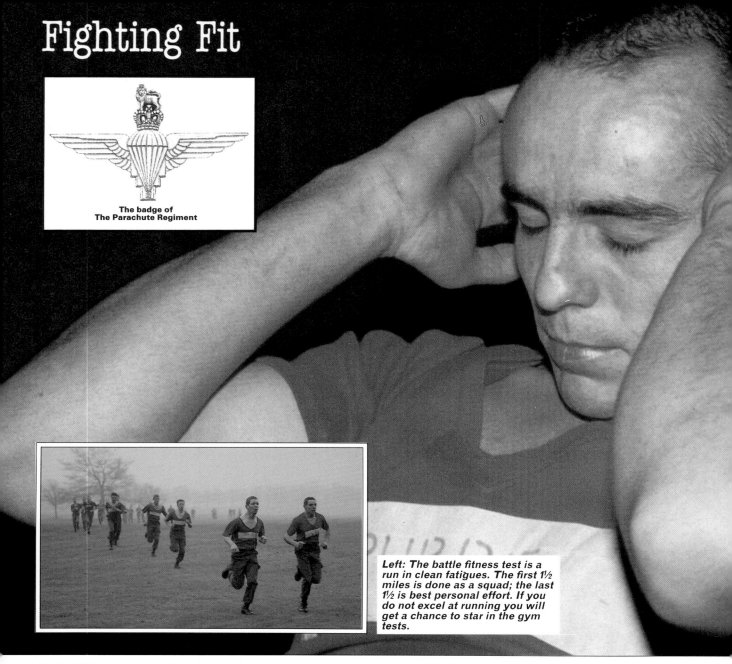

The badge of
The Parachute Regiment

Left: The battle fitness test is a run in clean fatigues. The first 1½ miles is done as a squad; the last 1½ is best personal effort. If you do not excel at running you will get a chance to star in the gym tests.

What it takes to be a Para
MARCH AND SHOOT

In Week 22 you return to depot life, with the emphasis on weapon training, PT and drill. The training staff have just four days in which to teach you how to handle the 7.62-mm General Purpose Machine-Gun (GPMG). Although the LSW has largely taken over from the GPMG, the older weapon still has its place, particularly when used in the sustained fire (SF) role.

By the end of the week you will have learned how the machine-gun operates. You will be shown how to strip and re-assemble it, how to load

and unload, and how to make safe. You will be taught how to use the sights, and learn the correct way of holding, aiming and firing the weapon. You will practise carrying out the Immediate Action (IA) and stoppage drills, and finally spend a day and a half on the ranges putting into practice all you have been shown.

In contrast to the LSW, the GPMG looks old-fashioned. It's longer and considerably heavier – weighing in at 12 kg as opposed to the LSW's 7 kg. After handling the SA80 system it takes some getting used to the GPMG's

awkward link ammunition belt and the lack of a handy SUSAT optical sight. And as for the recoil . . .! Difficult to understand how the training staff have nothing but praise for the outdated weapon.

The GPMG

The fact is, the GPMG is a battle-tried and proven weapon that has seen service throughout the world. Big and heavy it may be, and slightly antiquated, but as a reliable killing machine it has few equals. There are those amongst the staff who have seen

1138

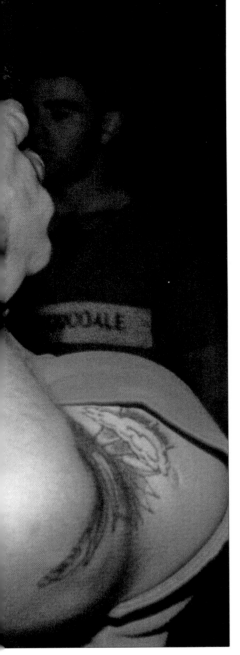

'Number ones out behind the gun!' The GPMG drills are practised with the class split into teams to add an air of competition. Speed will come with practice.

The gym test finds out how many repetitions of a particular exercise you can do in two minutes, with 30 seconds to recover between each exercise. It is a test of maximum effort and you had better beat your last score. Once you have finished, you change over in your pair and shout out for your partner.

its awesome power at first hand. They know what it is capable of. Nobody as yet knows how the LSW will perform when the chips are down.

In addition to learning the GPMG, you re-acquaint yourselves with the platoon PTI. Week 22 begins with 90 minutes of Battle Fitness Training (BFT) combined with the Army Personal Fitness Assessment (APFA), during which you have to complete a 1½-mile run in light order in less than 11 minutes, followed immediately by a series of tests in the gymnasium.

Each man is marked according to his performance during several exercises – sit-ups, bar-dips and pull-ups – while a vertical jump test determines how high you can jump from a standing position.

By comparing the results with those of BFT/APFA Week 1, the PTI gets a good idea of your improved fitness over the last 4½ months. Most of you are confident that you have done well. Some of you, perhaps, are getting just a bit over-confident. You're in for a rude awakening the next day.

Tuesday morning is an eight-mile March and Shoot competition. By 0815 you're all sitting in a coach that will take you to nearby Henley Park Ranges. Just before it leaves, the platoon commander climbs on board.

'I have just carried out an inspection of the floor, and it is sopping . . .!' he roars.

Oh dear.

'There will be an inspection first thing tomorrow morning at a time yet to be confirmed . . .'

When the officer finishes his tirade, one of the section corporals addresses the men. He tells you that *he* will conduct an inspection too, at 2100 hrs that evening! Bloody marvellous . . .

Forming up

The coach starts up and rolls out through the camp gates. You all stare morosely through the windows.

Arriving at Henley Park, you de-bus and each section hurriedly zeroes its weapons before forming up for inspection on the nearby road. Points are deducted for missing items of equipment, and for those whose webbing contents weigh less than the stipulated 12 kg.

You move out with the first section at 0945 hrs, to be followed at timed intervals by the others. The route is across the usual undulating type of terrain: rough countryside and the occasional road. It's certainly no more difficult than anything encountered in the past, and is certainly easier than anything in P Company. The pace is a bit brisk, but eight miles shouldn't present a problem.

But on your way back you begin to meet stragglers from the other sections who have dropped behind before even reaching the halfway point! Some of them seem to be having serious problems just to keep moving. You, too, now begin to feel the strain.

An NCO carefully weighs everyone's webbing before the start of the competition. It is better to be comfortably over weight: to be found under weight would be indicative of a serious attitude problem.

Fighting Fit

The last two or three miles are a real struggle. Many of you are breathing heavily and pouring with sweat.

Your NCO pushes relentlessly on, uncomplaining as always. The staff are all older than the recruits, yet none shows any sign of weakening. They never do at any point during your training. Clearly, there is something to be learned from this.

The debrief

Afterwards, the general opinion among the platoon is that everyone's fitness has deteriorated because of the relative inactivity of Brize Norton. The feeling among the staff is that those who found the effort too much simply haven't yet developed the proper mental attitude that comes with maturity and experience.

You stagger in to the finish at 1100 — one and three-quarter hours after starting the course! Your kit is again checked and weighed, and there is a 15-minute penalty for each man who fails to finish with his section. The shoot itself then begins, with each group lining up along the range's 300-metre firing point. The section's two LSW men are allowed two minutes to double to the 200-metre firing point, from where they must burst 12 balloon targets. After two minutes, or before if all the balloons are hit, the rest of you are given three minutes to double forward and hit 10 clay pigeon targets.

The shoot

The maximum score for first place in the shoot is 290 points. Top marks

You can't start firing until the whole team have got their belt buckles down on the firing point, so run down at the speed of the slowest man.

for the march are 250. The winning section is the one with the highest combined score at the end of the morning.

As the LSW men sprint forward, you get your breath back. It doesn't take the gunners long to dispose of the balloons.

As soon as the last is burst, you all race across the wet ground and fling yourselves down along the firing point. You force yourself to breathe more slowly while striving to keep the tiny target still within the sight picture. The black disc wavers in front of the sight's aiming point. How did people ever manage with the SLR, in the days before SUSAT sights? A shot rings out, and then another, as your mates begin firing. You take aim, and squeeze the trigger . . .

The SUSAT sight on the SA80 is considerably better than iron sights for static targets. The bad news is the run-down ruins your breathing for the shoot.

The rifle kicks slightly against your shoulder and . . . Missed! Bloody hell! Right, calm down. Relax. Aim again. Okay, steady . . . steady . . . deep breath . . . exhale . . . Fire! The target disintegrates. Great! On to the next one . . . The 10 clays are soon destroyed, and you are ordered to unload and clear weapons before moving off the range.

The next team lines up along the firing point, allowing you to sit back for a few minutes and enjoy a welcome mug of steaming hot tea.

Now, what time's that floor inspection?

Combat Report
Oman:
Surrounded at Mirbat

John McKenzie is a serving member of the British Special Forces and tells of one battle in the Oman campaign during the late 1970s.

Being a member of the military training team in Mirbat, near the coast of Oman, had become (to say the least) boring. Mirbat was a small town consisting of flat-topped buildings, with a coiled barbed-wire perimeter fence. The nearest provincial town was Salalah, about 45 miles to our west. During our three months in the town there had been two mortar attacks, but neither had caused any serious damage.

At times the heat had been almost unbearable and the flies and dust were always a nuisance, but now everyone was in good spirits. This was to be our last night in Oman: we were to be relieved the next morning and flown back to Britain. Little did we know that we were about to become involved in one of the fiercest battles of this 18-year campaign.

As we were getting into our sleeping bags, 300 guerrillas armed with AK-47s, Carl Gustav anti-tank guns, mortars, anti-tank rifles and heavy and light machine-guns were mustering for a full frontal attack on our position. Even with our complement of Askaris and men from the Dhofar Gendarmerie we totalled only 60 men. The guerrillas broke into groups and approached the town from all sides. We were completely surrounded and there was no possiblility of escape.

Four Strikemasters appeared

The first we knew of the attack was when mortar bombs rained down around us. The noise was deafening and was quickly accompanied by heavy machine-gun fire. For a few seconds there was total confusion as the mortar bombs fell around us, but we quickly got out of our sleeping bags, donned our desert boots and, carrying as much ammunition as we could manage, ran out of our billets with our weapons. We climbed on top of the flat roofs to get a good look and assess the situation.

As far as the eye could see there were muzzle flashes from automatic weapons and mortar barrels. There were swarms of guerrillas surrounding us and the odds appeared overwhelming. All we could do was fight hard and pray for luck.

Dave Billingham opened up with a heavy

Iran provided pilots and aircraft to help in Oman's fight, but some of the pilots weren't perfect: this Huey crashed through pilot error.

calibre .50 Browning machine-gun while the rest of us used our automatic FNs and picked off the leading guerrillas. As the first wave of them fell to the ground, they were replaced by a second and then a third – they just kept charging. In the meantime, a trooper had run to the World War II 25-pounder near the main boundary wire and began to operate it. As the old gun pounded away large numbers of the guerrillas either fell to the ground or were blown backwards, but were replaced by even more men. They were now only a few yards from the perimeter fence and there seemed no hope of stopping their advance.

Dave Roberts, although seriously wounded in the chest, propped himself up against a wall and continued to blast away with his FN. Our mortars fired high explosives and phosphorus at the guerrillas' heavy machine-gun and mortar positions. The fire fight had lasted continuously for about 40 minutes but there was no sign of the enemy being deterred by their heavy casualties, and they were now climbing over the perimeter fence.

Unknown to us, Captain Peters had been able to get to the radio and call in an air strike. Four Strikemasters suddenly appeared over our heads, at very low level under the cloud base. The pilots were all RAF officers on secondment and their flying skills were unique. They dropped 500-lb bombs on to the advancing enemy, blowing men, equipment and earth high into the air. The aircraft then banked around and, with their cannon, strafed the perimeter wire. One of the Strikemasters was hit by a hail of machine-gun fire. It banked violently to the left and managed to limp for home. Having completed their action, the remaining three joined the damaged aircraft and headed away.

Sporadic gunfire continued

A helicopter, coming to evacuate the wounded, appeared on the horizon. A green smoke grenade was thrown on the landing area to signal to the pilot where to put down. As the chopper came closer, it was raked by small-arms fire, causing a row of bullet holes along its starboard side. With this, a red smoke grenade was thrown on to the helipad, telling the pilot to bug out. The pilot spun the helicopter around and made off at high speed. He was quickly inside the cover of the low cloud base.

Although because of their suicide-line attacks most of the enemy were now either dead, wounded or retreating, sporadic gunfire still remained as we chose our targets at random.

Oman's coastal plain looks inhospitable enough but in the mountains scorching daytime heat was matched by extreme cold at night.

Another helicopter arrived and safely touched down after receiving its signal to land. The British wounded were all put on board and the pilot given the signal to go. Ten minutes later, a third helicopter landed. 'G' Squadron were on board and they immediately attacked the remaining pockets of resistance. With the appearance of these reinforcements, it was obvious to the guerrillas that it was all over, and within a very short time the battle was over. Official records later showed that this battle had lasted for a mere 90 minutes. Fighting for our survival as we had been, that 90 minutes had seemed like days. British casualties were few: two dead – Dave Roberts, who had died of his massive chest injuries in hospital, and the trooper who had manned the 25-pounder and who had been blasted by heavy-calibre machine-gun fire during the closing stages of the battle – and three seriously wounded.

The bodies of nearly 70 guerrillas were found at the foot of the perimeter fence, but their death toll is thought to have been almost double this. After this battle, the guerrillas were so demoralised that they never again attempted to mount such a large attack. In fact, the heavy casualties suffered during this battle broke the back of the Communist-backed campaign in Oman.

A Strikemaster in Omani colours flies over the Jebel armed with two 500-lb bombs and rockets for ground attack. Pilots were usually RAF on loan.

Fighting Fit

The badge of The Parachute Regiment

What it takes to be a Para
WELCOME TO THE AIRBORNE BROTHERHOOD

Your final week at the depot is spent rehearsing for the Passing Out Parade on Thursday morning. To the uninitiated, marching looks so simple. But it's bloody hard work keeping in step, because you not only have to concentrate on your own pace but on that of the men around you. As for rifle drill, well, it takes many days to perfect and constant practice to maintain. It's tiring, repetitious work, but necessary if your drill is to be faultless – and faultless it will be!

At last, after 23 weeks – six months – the big moment arrives. After all the effort, the sweat and pain, the doubt and fear, this is it! Some of you have gone through *two years* of one retraining platoon after another to reach this stage! Few have succeeded in staying the course from the very beginning.

Of the 60 recruits in the original complement of 531 Platoon, only 20 per cent – 12 men – have made it to the end. Of the rest, many have left the army, some have ended up as retrainers, a few have transferred.

Including those who joined the platoon from retrainers and elsewhere, a total of 91 recruits has made up the number at one time or another during the past 23 weeks. Of these, just 26 will pass out with 531.

The final inspection

By 1000 hrs on Thursday morning you are formed up outside the block for the sergeant major's inspection. This takes place in advance of the parade itself, thus ensuring a spotless turn-out. The sergeant major closely

Eyes right as you pass the dais: you look the reviewing officer straight in the eye as you pass him, and wait for the order 'eyes front'. You no longer have to think about it; the drill is automatic.

opposite a dais central of the guests' section. After being brought to open order, you right dress and cover off. You stand at ease and order arms while awaiting the arrival of the Inspecting General. When he appears at the edge of the square you are ordered to attention. You present arms, shoulder arms and the platoon commander then marches across to report.

Sadly, your own officer is unable to participate in the parade. A week previously he injured his arm during a rugby match and is now forced to watch the proceedings from the sidelines. Another officer accompanies the General on his inspection of the platoon. Satisfied with your turn-out, the General then marches over to inspect the band.

The march past

When the inspection comes to an end, the platoon is marched past the dais in a splendid display of precision drill. As you approach the dais the order is given for "Eyes right". You catch fleeting glimpses of your proud audience: mothers, fathers, brothers, sisters and friends. You, too, swell with pride. A good feeling.

Then comes the awards ceremony, in which prizes are presented for the champion recruit and champion shots on both the SA80 and LSW. The general then makes a short speech. He tells you what you already know: namely, what fine soldiers you all are! The padre blesses the platoon, and the platoon commander finally marches forward and requests permission to march off the square. Permission granted, he marches to the front of the platoon.

The best recruit receives his reward from the General. An Army photographer is on hand to record the event.

"In close order, right dress!"

"Eyes front".

"Move to the right in threes, right turn!"

The band strikes up and you are led to the top end of the square, where you left wheel for a final march past. You continue past the dais and all the way off the parade ground, back to the accommodation.

It's all over. The relief is immense. Big smiles all round as you congratulate yourselves on an impeccable display.

Although the parade is over, there are still two more displays scheduled for the benefit of your families. One is

The platoon sergeant wearing the general service medal and the South Atlantic medal is right marker for the platoon: a reminder that, not too long ago, young paratroopers passed off this square to fight in the Falklands.

examines each man in turn, before addressing the platoon.

"Yours is the best Platoon I've seen since I arrived here . . ." he tells you.

Tremendous praise, not bestowed lightly. What a guy!

The passing out ceremony is always a great social event. Your families and friends have been arriving at the depot all morning. By 1045 they're all seated along the edge of the parade square. Around a corner, waiting out of sight, is the platoon.

The band strikes up and leads you out onto the square. You march across the centre of the square and are halted

The paradrop from the sea King provides the parents and families with the opportunity to see their offspring in a spectacular display of their newly-learned skills.

The parachute display team the Red Devils put in a spectacular and accurate appearance while you prepare for your drop.

to be a parachute drop by the platoon from a Sea King helicopter over nearby Queen's Avenue. While you quickly change into working dress, your families are entertained by another, free-fall, parachute display by the Regiment's own Red Devils. They exit from 12,000ft above the depot to land directly in front of an appreciative audience.

When the display is over, the guests are treated to a tour of the regimental museum before boarding coaches for the short drive to Queen's Avenue.

As the transport pulls off the road onto the neighbouring playing fields, those on board are just in time to see the first stick emplane. The helicopter lifts slowly into the air, rapidly gaining height as it thuds across the field. Within minutes it is circling above the crowd of upturned faces. It approaches the DZ. The first man tumbles through the exit, quickly followed by another... There are oohs and aahs from the captivated audience...

Those of you in the air feel quite heroic when your turn arrives. It's certainly different from jumping out of a Herc. You have to take care not to catch the top of your parachute pack as you go out of the door. Then you are falling almost vertically; there's very little slipstream. Your parachute seems to deploy a lot sooner than expected, too. The rest is about the same as any descent – except for all those faces staring up at you. Better

give them a good landing then... Bang! Ooph! Well, it wasn't bad.

You collapse the canopy and pack away the 'chute before walking off the DZ. Beaming faces greet your return. You smile back and feel extremely pleased with yourself.

As soon as the last man has completed his descent, the coaches ferry you all back to camp for lunch. Then an hour in the Juniors' Mess Bar, before the platoon returns to the block for a final clean-up. Afterwards, 531 Platoon disperses for the last time.

Busy year ahead

As you are lucky to have completed training so near Christmas, you have three weeks' leave to look forward to. In early January you will return to Aldershot, where some of you are destined to join 3 Para. The majority, however, are to go to 1 Para. For the latter, 1988 promises to be a busy year, opening with an exercise in Kenya. This will be followed by a tour in Northern Ireland and then another exercise, in Oman. After Oman, you can look forward to a spell in the United States!

Whatever happens, you know you can perform with confidence that comes with the prestige of belonging to one of the world's finest fighting units: The Parachute Regiment!

531 Platoon, together for the last time before they pass off the square to pursue their military careers in Britain's elite airborne forces.